how2become

Electrical
Comprehension Tests

www.How2Become.com

As part of this product you also receive FREE access to online tests that will help you to pass Electrical Comprehension Tests.

To gain access, simply go to:

www.PsychometricTestsOnline.co.uk

Get more products for passing any test or interview at:

www.how2become.com

Orders: Please contact How2become Ltd, Suite 2, 50 Churchill Square Business Centre, Kings Hill, Kent ME19 4YU.

You can order through Amazon.co.uk under ISBN: 9781910602287 via the website www.How2Become.com or through Gardners.com.

ISBN: 9781910602287

First published in 2015 by How2become Ltd.

Typeset for How2become Ltd by Anton Pshinka.

Disclaimer

Every effort has been made to ensure that the information contained within this guide is accurate at the time of publication. How2become Ltd are not responsible for anyone failing any part of any selection process as a result of the information contained within this guide. How2become Ltd and their authors cannot accept any responsibility for any errors or omissions within this guide, however caused. No responsibility for loss or damage occasioned by any person acting, or refraining from action, as a result of the material in this publication can be accepted by How2become Ltd.

The information within this guide does not represent the views of any third party service or organisation.

CONTENTS

INTRODUCTION TO YOUR GUIDE

NTRODUCTION TO YOUR GUIDE

Welcome to your new guide, Electrical Comprehension Tests. This guide is a professional testing book which will assist you through your preparation for any Electrical Comprehension assessment.

Foremost, an Electrical Comprehension test is used to assess levels of technical and electrical knowledge. This type of test is commonly used for jobs involving electrical or engineering work, whereby knowledge of electrical mechanisms and concepts are required.

Within an Electrical Comprehension test, you will be assessed on how well you can articulate yourself in terms of electrical comprehension. Having technical knowledge is a requirement for certain types of job roles, and so it is important that you are able to highlight your skills in a competent and professional manner. The complexity of the test will depend on the job for which you are applying. Here at How2become, our team of experts have done their utmost to ensure you have a guide packed full of insightful information and sample questions, that will guarantee to improve your performance in any Electrical Comprehension test.

The key to success is to try your hardest to get 100% in the test which you are undertaking. If you aim for 100% in your preparation, then you are far more likely to score high marks when it comes to taking your assessment. If you are serious about passing your assessment, you will need to put the time and effort into your preparation, in order to achieve great results.

By the end of this book, you will be able to:

- Demonstrate a basic understanding in relation to technical and electrical concepts;
- Understand the meaning of electrical signs and what they represent;
- Understand the importance of electrical safety and the dangers involved;
- Illustrate the important concepts in relation to electrical components including: currents, voltages, resistances, energy and circuits;
- Improve your knowledge and understanding of electrical concepts;
- Engage with the basics of electrical comprehension and advance your knowledge to show stronger levels of understanding.

ABOUT
ELECTRICAL
COMPREHENSION

WHAT ARE ELECTRICAL COMPREHENSION TESTS?

As part of recruitment processes, you may be required to undertake an Electrical Comprehension test. Electrical Comprehension is quite self-explanatory; you will be required to undertake a series of testing questions that assess your electrical understanding.

Electrical Comprehension tests are specifically designed to measure your performance in relation to electrical concepts. You need to engage with, and utilise, your skills and knowledge, and illustrate the key competencies and qualities required for particular job roles.

During an Electrical Comprehension test, you are likely to encounter the following types of questions:

Simple Circuits	Electrical Symbols	Switches	Lamps
Electrical Safety	Hazard Perception	Electrical Energy	Currents
Voltages	Resistance	Resistors	Diodes
Electrical Measurements	Process Flow	Signal Flow	Potential Difference
Electrical Schematics	Ohm's Law	Electrons	Ammeter
Units of Electricity	Particles	Atoms	Energy Transfers

WHO SITS AN ELECTRICAL COMPREHENSION TEST?

Any job that requires strong levels of electrical knowledge will often expect you to undertake an Electrical Comprehension test. Employers need to safeguard themselves with employees who show potential and will be able to perform the role to a strong level and to a high professional standard.

An Electrical Comprehension test is often used alongside other psychometric tests during the RAF Airman assessments. The Royal Air Force entails a whole range of skills, including those of a technical ability. You'll be working with high-end electrical equipment, so it is imperative that you are able to demonstrate great knowledge and performance in relation to electrical ability.

As well as the Royal Air Force, there are many other jobs and even academic studies, which need candidates to possess strong levels of electrical backgrounds. Other areas that may use an Electrical Comprehension test during their initial selection process include the following:

- Armed Forces;
- Technical Positions;
- Electricians;
- Signal Repairers;
- Wireman;
- Engineers;
- Electrical Engineering;
- Physics.

Please note, the above list is not exhaustive. There may be other jobs that ask you to undertake an Electrical Comprehension test. It is important that, when applying for a job, you understand the selection process involved, in order to maximise your potential and increase your chances of success.

If you know that you have to sit an Electrical Comprehension test, it is imperative that you make the most of the preparation time prior to your assessment. Engage with practice tests to ensure that you are fully prepared and your performance is improved.

WHY AM I BEING ASSESSED?

Electrical Comprehension tests are specifically designed to assess a particular set of skills, intellect and qualities required to work within an electrical and technical post.

The reason why you are being assessed in this manner is simple; if you score high marks on an Electrical Comprehension test, then you are far more likely to perform better in the job role.

Electrical aptitude tests have become a popular psychometric assessment for many electrical-related job positions. Employers want to ensure that their time, money and effort are put into candidates who show willingness to obtain a career of high technical standards, and excel in their performance on a day-to-day basis.

Not only does electrical aptitude testing assess intellectual ability, it is also a way to measure competency, proficiency and professionalism. The equipment used in relation to such technical posts is vastly costly. Employers need to expose such expensive and advanced technical equipment to candidates who show capability of using such apparatuses.

HOW TO PREPARE FOR AN ELECTRICAL COMPREHENSION TEST

The best way to prepare for an Electrical Comprehension test, or any other form of psychometric test, is to simply practice prior to your assessment. Ultimately, the more you practice, the more likely you are to achieve higher scores and thus improve your overall performance.

Here at How2become, we have done our utmost to provide you with a guide packed full of sample questions both of a basic and advanced standard, in order to improve and enhance your overall understanding.

STRUCTURE OF THE BOOK

In order to make the most out of your Electrical Comprehension testing guide, we have created a guide that follows a clear and simple structure which contains lots of sample questions to aid you through your preparation period.

For this guide, we have laid out its contents as formulated below:

- Introduction to your guide;
- About Electrical Comprehension tests;
- Preparing for Electrical Comprehension;
- **The Basics of Electrical Comprehension;**
  - o Detailed example questions;
  - o 4 testing sections;
  - o Detailed answers and explanations;

- **Advanced Electrical Comprehension;**
    - o Detailed example questions;
    - o 4 testing sections;
    - o Detailed answers and explanations;
- A Few Final Words…

PREPARING
FOR
ELECTRICAL
COMPREHENSION

HINTS AND TIPS

There is no doubt that you will struggle with electrical aptitude tests if you have no prior knowledge of technical and electrical concepts.

You need to ensure yourself with the best preparation in order to secure the job position for which you have applied. It is imperative that you take the time, and focus on what is expected in terms of completing your assessment to a high standard.

The following is a list of tips and/or useful advice that you should consider in order to provide yourself with the best preparation for your assessment:

- Carry out lots of sample testing questions which focus on the subject you are preparing for. For electrical tests, it is vitally important that you understand what the question is asking. You need to read the question carefully to ensure you have read it correctly.

- Whilst undertaking sample tests, it is important that, if you get a question wrong, you spend time working out why you got it wrong. In this guide, we have provided answers and detailed explanations to assist you through your learning process. If you get a question wrong, consider *why* you have got it wrong. Read through the answers and explanations in order to improve your overall knowledge.

- When practising, you must ensure that you work on your speed as well as your accuracy. Most tests are administered under time limits, and therefore you will be expected to answer as many questions as possible within the allotted time given. However, you do not want to sacrifice the accuracy of your answers. Do not rush through the questions; you want to avoid making careless mistakes.

- The majority of tests will be in a multiple-choice format. You want to steer away from wild-guesses. Wild-guesses will come at a price, and you will lose marks for incorrect answers.

- Some questions may ask you to draw or sketch an electrical component. Make sure that your drawing is clear and labelled.

When preparing for an Electrical Comprehension test, you should spend an adequate amount of time practising circuit questions and symbol questions. Circuit questions are the basic foundations of any electrical test, and are often used to assess basic understanding of electrical components. Symbol questions refer to components found within circuits, such as resistors, lamps, fuses, amplifiers etc. These types of questions form the very basics of electrical understandings, and therefore you need to master these to a high standard to even be considered for a job post.

- Aim for 100% in your answers. If you aim for 100% in your test, then you are far more likely to achieve the trade or career that you want.

- Confidence is an important part of test preparation. Have you ever sat a timed test and your mind goes blank? This is because your mind is focused on negative thoughts and your belief that you will fail. If you practice plenty of test questions under timed conditions, then your confidence will increase. If your confidence is at its peak, then you are more likely to perform to a higher standard.

- Having a basic GCSE understanding of physics and electronics will be an advantage. You need to feel fully equipped to tackle the questions and score highly on the assessment. Brush up on the basics of physics, circuits and electronics.

- It is important that you learn and practice the different types of electrical questions that you are likely to encounter on the job. Work out what electrical knowledge is required for the job for which you are applying, and focus your preparation around these areas.

Finally, we have also provided you with some additional free online psychometric tests which will help to further improve your competence in this particular testing area. To gain access, simply go to:

www.PsychometricTestsOnline.co.uk

Good luck and best wishes,

The how2become team

The How2become team

THE **BASICS** OF ELECTRICAL COMPREHENSION

n this section of the guide, we will provide you with testing questions that have been specifically created to guide you through the basics of electrical aptitude tests.

For any Electrical Comprehension test, it is important that you master the basics. With 100 questions for you to practice, this guide will assist you through your preparation period, and ultimately improve your performance.

Within this section, we have focused on the following areas:

- Circuits;
- Electrical Symbols;
- Series and Parallel Circuits;
- Alternating and Direct Currents;
- Voltages;
- Resistance;
- Resistors;
- Diodes.

Before you begin practising, take a look at the following example pages for **basic** Electrical Comprehension. The examples include useful information in relation to the types of questions you will encounter. Moreover, the examples show you how to work out the questions, the representation of symbols, and include insightful advice and tips on how to answer the questions successfully.

EXAMPLES OF BASIC ELECTRICAL COMPREHENSION

For any Electrical Comprehension test, it is important that you have grasped the concept of each electrical symbol. You will be required to have a solid understanding of what each symbol represents, and what they mean in terms of electrical functionality.

An Electrical Comprehension test is guaranteed to assess your intellectual ability in relation to certain symbols, and so we have provided you with the symbols that we believe will cover the basics of any Electrical Comprehension test. Below, we have put together a glossary, that includes definitions of electrical components.

CIRCUIT SYMBOLS

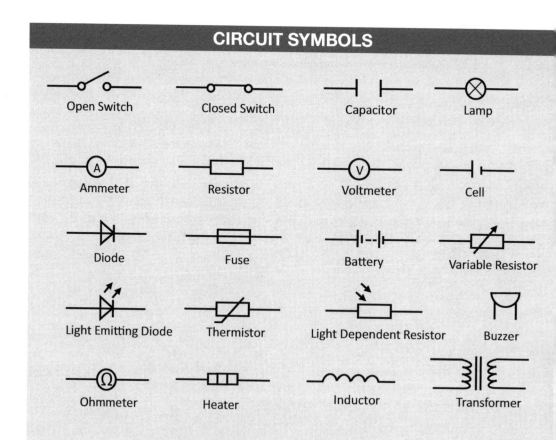

GLOSSARY

- **Alternating current:** an alternating current (AC) is a current that is continuously changing direction.

- **Ammeter:** an ammeter is an electrical unit that measures current. An ammeter needs to be connected in series.

- **Battery:** a battery supplies the electrical charge of a circuit. A battery contains more than one cell (see cell for definition).

- **Buzzer:** a buzzer is a transducer which converts energy into sound.

- **Capacitor:** a capacitor stores the electrical charge of the circuit. It can be used alongside a resistor in a 'timing' circuit. It acts as a sort of 'filter', whereby it blocks direct current (DC) signals, but permits alternating current (AC) signals running through the circuit.

- **Cell:** a cell is the component of a circuit that supplies the electrical charge. The larger terminal of the symbol represents the positive element and the smaller terminal represents the negative element. More than one cell = battery.

- **Closed switch:** a closed switch allows a current to flow through a circuit. This is done by closing the switch, which is what you would call an 'on switch' (i.e. it has the power to turn the circuit 'on').

- **Conductor:** an electrical conductor is anything or any material which can carry an electrical current. Other conductors may conduct heat.

- **Diode:** a diode is an electrical device that only permits current flow in one direction.

- **Direct current:** a direct current can be established if the current flows in one direction. For example, batteries and solar cells supply direct currents, with a typical battery supplying 1.5V.

- **Electron:** a subatomic particle that carries the smallest of magnitudes of negative electricity.

- **Fuse:** a fuse acts as a 'safety device' for electrical circuits. The fuse will blow, i.e. melt, if the current flowing through the circuit exceeds a specified amount.

- **Heater:** a heater is a transducer that converts electrical energy into heat.

- **Inductor:** an inductor is an output device which includes a coil of wire that subsequently creates a magnetic field when a current passes through. It can often be used as a transducer to convert electrical energy into mechanical energy by this idea of 'pulling on something'.

- **Insulator:** an insulator is a material which acts as a very poor conductor of electricity. Electrical wires are often covered with an insulating material in order to guard the circuit's electrical supply and provide a safety precaution to people using them.

- **Lamp:** a lamp, or a bulb, is used as a transducer which converts the electrical energy within a circuit to permit light. This is often used within cars to indicate a warning light on the dashboard.

- **Light dependent resistor:** a light dependent resistor, or a photoresistor, is a light-controlled variable. They change resistance as the light level changes.

- **Light emitting diode:** often abbreviated as LED, light emitting diode is a transducer which converts energy into light.

- **Ohmmeter:** ohmmeter is a device that measures resistance.

- **Ohm's law:** Ohm's law states that the current in a circuit between two points is directly proportional to the voltage and inversely proportional to resistance.

- **Open switch:** an open switch prevents a current from flowing through the circuit.

- **Resistor:** a resistor is a term that is self-explanatory. It restricts the flow of the current. For example, a resistor can be used to restrict the flow of current in an LED.

- **Thermistor:** a thermistor is an input device relating to sensors. It is a transducer which converts temperature and heat into resistance, i.e. an electrical property.

- **Transformer:** a transformer is a type of power supply. It contains two coils of wiring which are linked by an iron core. It is used to increase or decrease alternating current (AC) voltages. The transformer transfers energy through magnetic fields, not electrical fields.

- **Variable resistor:** a variable resistor is used to control the current flow. This type of resistor contains two contacts. The resistor permits the control of adjusting lamp brightness and motoring speed.

- **Voltmeter:** a voltmeter is an electrical unit that measures voltage. This is also known as 'potential difference'.

SERIES / PARALLEL CIRCUITS

It is important that you are able to differentiate between series circuits and parallel circuits. To distinguish between these two types of circuits, you should remember the following points:

- If there are no branches, then it is a **series** circuit;
- If there are branches, it is a **parallel** circuit.

Fairy lights

Series circuits can be described using the example of fairy lights. It is an electrical circuit in which the devices are connected end-to-end. It only has one path of flow.

Any break in the series of lights, results in no flow of electricity. In other words, if one light in the sequence breaks, the others will stop working.

Homes

Parallel circuits means more than one path of flow.

For example, in order to use multiple devices in your home, you use multiple paths of wiring that connects to an electrical circuit. This allows you to continue watching TV whilst turning off the lights.

ELECTRICAL CALCULATIONS

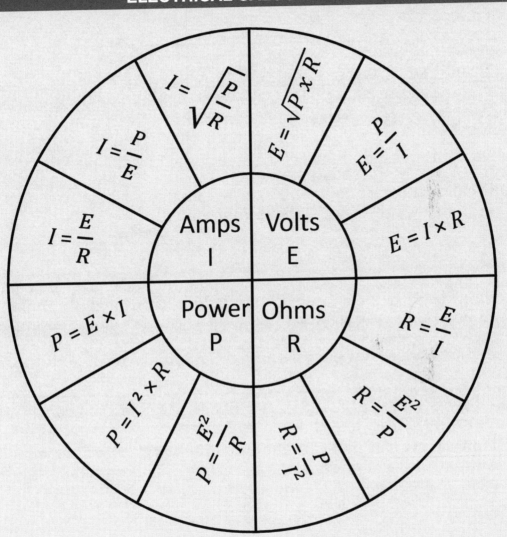

ATOMS AND PARTICLES

Everything is made up of atoms. Atoms comprise three particles:

- Protons;
- Neutrons;
- Electrons.

Neutrons – neutral.

Protons and electrons – electrically charged. Protons are positive, and electrons are negative.

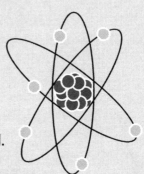

The number of protons in an atom is called its 'atomic number'.

The total number of electrons in an atom is the same number of the total number of protons in the nucleus. This means that atoms have no overall electrical charge. The nucleus is part of the atom that the particles surround.

ELECTRICAL HAZARDS

Electricity is a form of energy. You need to be fully aware of the dangers involved when using electrical components.

Below is a list of examples of ways in which you can be electrocuted if you are not careful when handling electricity:

- Pushing objects into plug sockets;
- Water touching an electrical compliance;
- Damaged wiring;
- Incorrect wiring;
- Overheated cables and plug sockets;
- Frayed cables.

CURRENTS

AC Electricity

Alternating currents (AC) can be defined through the changes in direction which the flow of electricity undertakes.

0V

The UK mains supply is approximately 230V, and has a frequency of 50Hz, which is equivalent to 50 changes in direction per second.

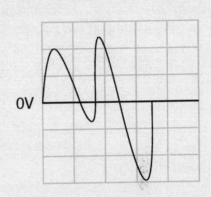

DC Electricity

Direct currents (DC) can be established if the current flows in one direction. For example, batteries and solar cells supply direct currents, with a typical battery supplying 1.5V.

0V

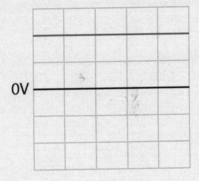

A current is the rate of flow, otherwise known as an **electrical charge.** No current is able to flow through the circuit if it is broken. For example, if a switch is open, this prevents an electrical charge from flowing. These currents flow when **electrons** move through a conductor i.e. a metal wire.

VOLTAGES

Voltage is also known as the **potential difference or electromotive force (e.m.f.).** The potential difference is needed to make an electrical current flow through an electrical component. For example, cells and batteries are often used to provide the potential difference needed in a circuit.

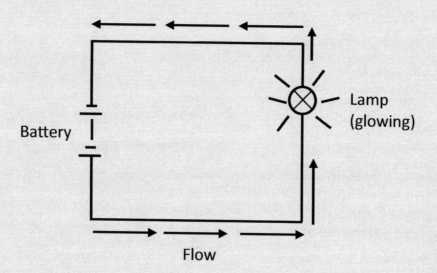

In the above electrical circuit, you will notice that there is only one source of potential difference (the battery). There is also only one source of resistance (the lamp).

RESISTANCE

The term resistance refers to an electrical element that measures its opposition to a current. A resistance to the flow of electricity in a circuit occurs in most conductors.

The resistance of a wire can be increased in two ways:

- Increasing the length of the wire;
- Decreasing the thickness of the wire.

The resistance of a **long** wire is greater than the resistance of a **short** wire. This is because the electrons collide more with ions as it passes through.

The resistance in a **thin** wire is greater than that of the resistance of a **thick** wire. This is because a thin wire has fewer electrons to carry the current flow.

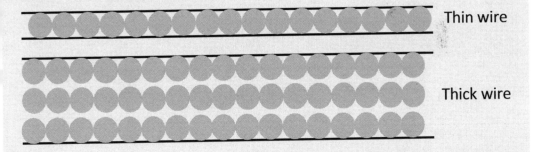

Thin wire

Thick wire

OHM's LAW

Ohm's law is often used to analyse the electrical components within a circuit. In simple terms, Ohm's law specifically focuses on three electrical concepts:

- Potential difference (voltage);
- Current;
- Resistance.

The resistance of an electrical outlet can be found by measuring the current flow and the potential difference, i.e. the voltage running through it.

There is a simple equation to use in order to work out the relationship between current, resistance and potential difference.

REMEMBER: the following equation:

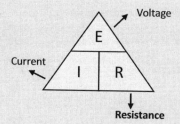

To work out the **resistance,** eliminate the 'R' from the equation:

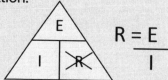

$$R = \frac{E}{I}$$

To work out the **current,** eliminate the 'I' from the equation:

$$I = \frac{E}{R}$$

To work out the **voltage,** eliminate the 'E' from the equation:

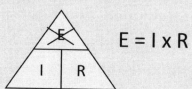

$$E = I \times R$$

BASICS –
TEST
SECTION 1

Question 1

Identify the following electrical symbol:

Answer   Fuse

Question 2

Identify the following electrical symbol:

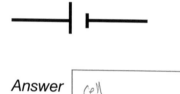

Answer   Cell

Question 3

Identify the following electrical symbol:

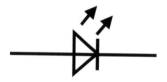

A – Diode.

B – Light dependent resistor.

C – Light emitting diode.

D – Variable resistor.

Answer   R

Question 4

What are the basic particles that make up an atom?

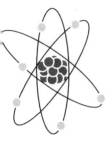

A – Protons, neutrons and particles.

B – Protons and electrons.

C – Neutrons, protons and electrons.

D – Mesons, neutrons and electrons.

Answer

Question 5

Which of the following statements best describes 'Ohm's Law'?

A – The total resistance in an electrical circuit.

B – $E = MC^2$.

C – An equation that converts energy into heat.

D – The relationship between current, voltage and resistance in an electrical circuit.

Answer

Question 6

In the following circuit, if switch A closes, and switch B remains open, wha
will happen?

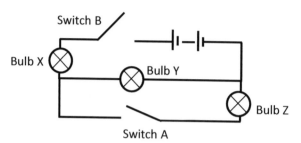

A – Bulbs X, Y, and Z will illuminate.

B – Bulb X will illuminate only.

C – Bulbs Y and Z will illuminate.

D – No bulbs will illuminate.

Answer

Question 7

A bicycle uses a battery operated light for its front and rear lights. The front
and rear lights are often of different sized bulbs. The filament in the rear lamp
has a resistance of 4 ohms. It takes a current of 0.3A. What voltage does the
lamp work at?

A – 1.8V.

B – 0.075V.

C – 0.7V.

D – 1.2V.

Answer

Question 8

What will be the voltage at point A, if the battery is 12 volts?

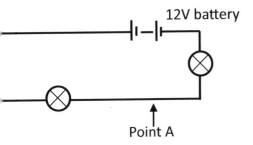

12V battery

Point A

A – 0 volts.

B – 3 volts.

C – 12 volts.

D – 6 volts.

Answer

Question 9

An atom's atomic number is determined by the number of what?

A – Neutrons.

B – Protons.

C – Electrons.

D – Atoms.

Answer

Question 10

In the following electrical circuit, if switch B closes, what will happen?

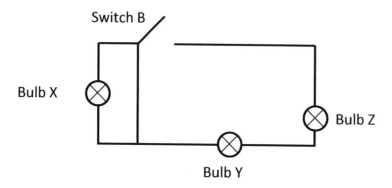

A – Bulbs X, Y, and Z will illuminate.

B – Bulb X will illuminate only.

C – Bulbs Y and Z will illuminate.

D – No bulbs will illuminate.

Answer

Question 11

Ammeters measure the amount of current in a circuit. In the circuit below, all of the ammeters are identical. If ammeter A1 reads 0.8A, what will ammeter A3 read?

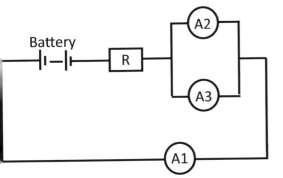

A – 0.12A.

B – 0.8A.

C – 0.4A.

D – 0.24A.

Answer

Question 12

What happens when an electrical charge flows through a resistor?

A – The temperature decreases.

B – The temperature increases.

C – The temperature fluctuates.

D – The temperature stays the same.

Answer

Question 13

What is the current in the circuit below?

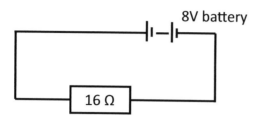

A – 2A.

B – 1.2A.

C – 0.5A.

D – 8A.

Answer [ ]

Question 14

Insert the two missing words:

Voltage is a measure of the difference in _____ _____ between two parts of a circuit. The bigger the difference in energy, the bigger the voltage.

A – Electrical current.

B – Flowing amperes.

C – Concurrent electricity.

D – Electrical energy.

Answer [ ]

Question 15

In the following circuit, how many bulbs will illuminate if switches 1 and 5 close?

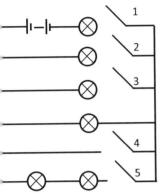

A – 2.

B – 3.

C – 4.

D – 5.

E – No bulbs will illuminate.

Answer

Question 16

Insert the two missing words:

At a low temperature, the resistance of a thermistor is _____ and allows for _____ current to flow through.

A – High, little.

B – Low, little.

C – High, more.

D – Low, more.

Answer A

Question 17

Computer monitors and television screens are often covered in dust because...

A – The dust is attracted by the cool air of the technological device.

B – Dust is unmanageable.

C – The dust is attracted to the microfibres of the screen.

D – The dust is attracted by the static charges compelling from the technological device.

Answer

Question 18

What is the voltage across the battery?

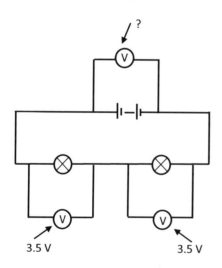

3.5 V   3.5 V

A – 3.5V.

B – 12.25V.

C – 7V.

D – 1.25V.

Answer

Question 19

Insert the two missing words:

Current is a measure of how much _ _ _ _ _ _ _ _ _ _ _ _ _ _ _ _ _ _ flows through a circuit. The more charge that flows, the bigger the current.

A – Electrical energy.

B – Electrical current.

C – Flowing amperes.

D – Electrical charge.

Answer

Question 20

Which of these diagrams of the ammeters is connected correctly?

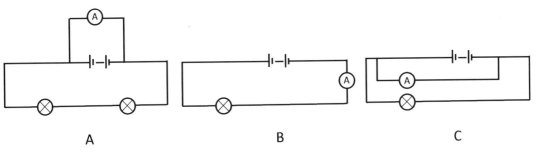

A	B	C
Diagram A	Diagram B	Diagram C

Question 21

The circuit below shows four identical ammeters. Fill in the missing blanks in the table in accordance with the circuit. Write your answers in the spaces provided in the table.

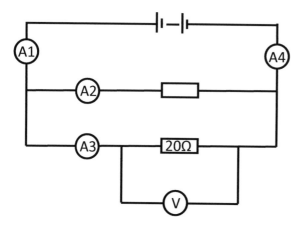

Ammer	Reading on Ammer
A1	1
A2	0.2
A3	0.3
A4	4

Question 22

In the circuit below, if one bulb blows, what would happen to the other bulbs in the circuit?

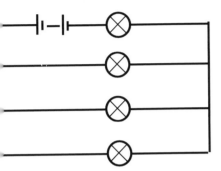

A	B	C	D
Stay lit, but dims	Stay lit, with same brightness	Stay lit, and brightens	No bulbs will illuminate

Question 23

Which of the following statements is true in relation to parallel circuits?

A – The resistance is shared between each of the components connected in parallel of the circuit.

B – The voltage is shared between each of the components connected in parallel of the circuit.

C – The current is shared between each of the components connected in parallel of the circuit.

D – None of the above.

Answer

Question 24

Electrical potential difference also means _ _ _ _ _ _ _ _ _ .

A – Current.

B – Resistance.

C – Voltage.

D – Parallel circuit.

Answer

Question 25

What does a transformer do to electrical currents?

A – Changes the voltage.

B – It turns electricity into power.

C – It adds more watts.

D – It conducts heat from the transformer component.

Answer

ANSWERS TO BASICS – TEST SECTION 1

Q1. Fuse

EXPLANATION = the symbol represents a fuse.

Q2. Cell

EXPLANATION = the symbol represents a cell.

Q3. C = light emitting diode

EXPLANATION = the symbol represents a light emitting diode.

Q4. C = neutrons, protons and electrons

EXPLANATION = an atom is made up of three small subatomic particles: neutrons, protons and electrons. The neutrons and protons make up the centre of the atom. The electrons hover and fly around the centre atom in a cloud-like formation.

Q5. D = the relationship between current, voltage and resistance in an electrical circuit

EXPLANATION = Ohm's law refers to the mathematical formula comprising of the relationships found between the current, voltage and resistance within an electronic circuit.

Q6. D = no bulbs will illuminate

EXPLANATION = if switch A closes, and switch B remains open, no bulbs will illuminate. Even with switch A being an 'on-switch', the fact that switch B remains open means that the power supply (i.e. the battery) cannot supply the power because the circuit is broken.

Q7. D = 1.2V

EXPLANATION = in order to work out the voltage, you need to multiply the resistance by the current. So, $4 \times 0.3 = 1.2V$.

Q8. C = 12 volts

EXPLANATION = in a series circuit, there is only one path for the current, and therefore that current is the same at all points of the path.

Q9. B = protons

EXPLANATION = an atomic number is determined by the number of protons in an atom's nucleus.

Q10. D = no bulbs will illuminate

EXPLANATION = the reason that no bulbs will illuminate is because, and although the switch would become an 'on-switch', there is no power source to generate anything, and therefore the bulbs would not be lit.

Q11. C = 0.4A

EXPLANATION = if ammeter A1 reads 0.8, then ammeters A2 and A3 will have to share this current, therefore each of these would read 0.4.

Q12. B = the temperature increases

EXPLANATION = when an electrical charge flows through a resistor, the temperature increases. The resistor gets hot from the electrical charge running through it, therefore increasing the temperature.

Q13. C = 0.5A

EXPLANATION = the current in this circuit is as follows: $8 \div 16 = 0.5A$.

Q14. D = electrical energy

EXPLANATION = the two words that are missing in the sentence are 'electrical energy'. Voltage is a measure of the difference in electrical energy between two parts of a circuit.

Q15. C = 4

EXPLANATION = if switches 1 and 5 were closed, 4 bulbs would illuminate. The bulb left of switch 1 would illuminate, the two bulbs left of switch 5 would illuminate, and the bulb on the fourth horizontal line would illuminate.

Q16. A = high, little

EXPLANATION = at a low temperature, the resistance of a thermistor is high, and little current can flow through. In comparison, at a high temperature, the resistance of a thermistor is low, and allows for more current to flow through.

Q17. D = the dust is attracted by the static charges compelling from the technological device

EXPLANATION = computer screens and television screens are often covered in dust because the dust becomes attracted by the static charges compelling from the technological device. The electrical element of statics can be demonstrated when two objects rub together and become 'electronically charged'. When you remove the dust, you often hear the static electricity snapping'.

Q18. C = 7V

EXPLANATION = the circuit contains two elements that share the voltage. Therefore, the overall voltage of the battery is as follows: 3.5 + 3.5 = 7V.

Q19. D = electrical charge

EXPLANATION = in order for the sentence to make sense, the two words that you would need to enter into the sentence are 'electrical charge'. So, the sentence would read 'current is a measure of how much electrical charge flows through a circuit. The more charge that flows, the bigger the current'.

Q20. B = diagram B

EXPLANATION = diagram B is wired correctly because ammeters need to be wired in a series circuit. The ammeter needs to be connected by one path of wiring.

Q21. A1 = 0.5, A4 = 0.5

EXPLANATION = A1 and A4 will both equal 0.5.

Q22. B = stay lit, with same brightness

EXPLANATION = if one of the bulbs goes out, it does not affect the other bulbs. The bulbs are all placed on different paths which are linked by the same battery. Therefore, if one path stops working, the others will continue to work. This does not affect the brightness of the bulbs as the bulbs are still powered by the same amount of power from the battery.

Q23. C = the current is shared between each of the components connected in parallel of the circuit.

EXPLANATION = within a parallel circuit, the current is shared amongst each component that is connected in parallel.

Q24.C = voltage

EXPLANATION = electrical potential difference is also the same as voltage. Voltage can be defined as measuring the difference in electrical energy.

Q25. A = changes the voltage

EXPLANATION = a transformer component within an electrical circuit is a device whereby it transfers energy between two or more circuits. With an alternating current, a transformer will increase or decrease the voltage as it makes the transfer.

BASICS –
TEST
SECTION 2

Question 1

Which electrical component is the following a description of?

A safety device which will blow, i.e. 'melt', if the current through it exceeds a specified value.

A – Battery.

B – Fuse.

C – Switch.

D – Bulb.

E – Resistor.

Answer

Question 2

Which of the following is NOT an effect of an electrical current?

A – Chemical.

B – Sound.

C – Heat.

D – Light.

Answer

Question 3

When an aeroplane is being refuelled, to avoid causing a spark which could build up from static charge...

A – The person pouring in the fuel needs to pour it in slowly.

B – The aeroplane has rubber tyres which insulates the charges.

C – The refuelling tank and the aeroplane itself are earthed.

D – The person pouring in the fuel needs to pour it in fast.

E – The person needs to be electronically uncharged.

Answer C

Question 4

What is wrong with the circuit shown below?

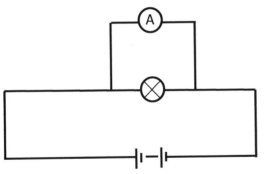

A – It is an incomplete circuit.

B – The ammeter needs to be connected in series.

C – The ammeter needs to be a voltmeter instead.

D – There is only one ammeter.

E – There is only one battery.

Answer B

Question 5

10 kilovolts is the equivalent to which of the following?

A – 10 millivolts.

B – 1.0 volts.

C – 1000 volts.

D – 10,000 volts.

E – 100 millivolts.

Answer

Question 6

How do you calculate energy transferred?

A	B	C
$E = I \times V \times T$	$E = V \div Q$	$E = I \div V \div T$

Question 7

How much energy is transferred in 20 seconds with a current of 16 amperes and the potential difference of 250 volts?

A – 80,000V.

B – 8,000J.

C – 8,000V.

D – 80,000J.

E – 80J.

Answer

Question 8

In the following circuit, if bulb 3 is removed and the switch is closed, which bulbs will illuminate?

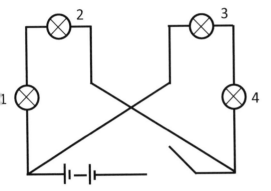

A – Bulb 4 will illuminate.

B – Bulbs 1, 2 and 4 will illuminate.

C – Bulbs 2 and 4 will illuminate.

D – Bulbs 1 and 2 will illuminate.

E – No bulbs will illuminate.

Answer

Question 9

Identify the following electrical symbol:

Answer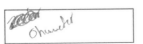

Question 10

Parallel circuits, like the diagram below, are useful because...

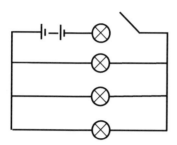

A	B	C
They require less wiring than series circuits.	They use less electricity.	Other components keep working even if one fails.

Question 11

Which circuit (A or B) has the smallest current?

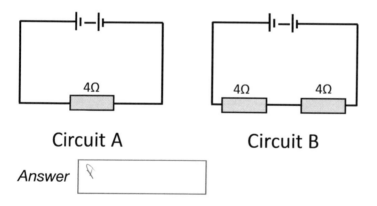

Circuit A   Circuit B

Answer

Question 12

Identify the following electrical symbol:

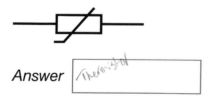

Answer   Thermistor

Question 13

Using the previous question, which of the following best describes the function of the symbol?

A – Used as a temperature sensor. The resistance decreases as the temperature increases.

B – Used as a temperature sensor. The resistance increases as the temperature increases.

C – Used as a temperature sensor. The current increases as the temperature increases.

D – Used as a temperature sensor. The current decreases as the temperature increases.

E – Used as a temperature sensor. The diode decreases as the temperature increases.

Answer

Question 14

Below is a list of materials. Which of the following answers is in the correct order of ability to conduct electricity. The best conductor of electricity should be written first, and the poorest conductor should be written last.

PVC   Aluminium   Silver   Water   Rubber   Copper

A – Copper, silver, aluminium, PVC, water, rubber.

B – Silver, aluminium, copper, PVC, rubber, water.

C – Silver, copper, aluminium, water, PVC, rubber.

D – Aluminium, copper, silver, PVC, rubber, water.

E – Aluminium, silver, copper, water, PVC, rubber.

Answer

Question 15

What is the effect of changing a wire in a circuit from a thick wire to a thin wire?

A	B	C
The bulbs will become brighter.	The bulbs will become dimmer.	The bulbs will stay the same.

Question 16

LEDs are being used more and more. What logical explanation can be used to determine why this might be?

A – They have a higher resistance.

B – They require a higher voltage.

C – They are more eco-friendly.

D – They use a smaller current.

E – They provide a larger current.

Answer

Question 17

When plastic is electronically charged by rubbing it with a cloth material, it can _____ small pieces of paper.

A – Attract.

B – Repel.

C – Charge.

D – Light.

Answer   A

Question 18

Current electricity occurs when _____ flow freely between more than one object.

A – Ions.

B – Electrons.

C – Neutrons.

D – Nucleus.

E – Voltage.

Answer   B

Question 19

If an electrical circuit is an analogue for a waterpark, that means the battery would be an analogue for _ _ _ _ _ _ .

A – The pump which supplies energy to move the water around.

B – The rate at which the water is pumped.

C – The speed at which the water flows.

D – The pipe which carries water through the circuit.

E – The restrictions of water flow.

Answer

Question 20

A simple circuit contains a light bulb and a battery. The current through the battery is...

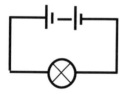

A – Less than the current through the light bulb.

B – More than the current through the light bulb.

C – The same as the current through the path of wiring.

D – The same as the current through the light bulb.

E – Less than the current through the path of wiring.

Answer

Question 21

Which of the following answers best describes the reason why birds are able to stand on high voltage electrical power lines?

A – The potential difference between the bird's feet is high.

B – They are aware of the power lines that are 'live', and those that are not.

C – Birds are an insulator.

D – They have complete resistance to the voltage.

E – The potential difference between the bird's feet is low.

Answer [E]

Question 22

In the following diagram, three light bulbs are connected to the same battery. Which of the following could you do to the circuit to increase the current being measured at point X?

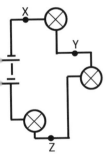

A – Increase the resistance of one of the bulbs.

B – Increase the resistance of two bulbs.

C – Add another bulb.

D – Remove one of the bulbs.

E – Increase the resistance of all three bulbs.

Answer [D]

Question 23

In electrical circuits, what do diodes regulate?

A	B	C
Potential difference	Resistance	Current

Question 24

What is the SI unit of capacitance?

A – Ohm.

B – Farad.

C – Watt.

D – Amps.

E – Joules.

Answer [ ]

Question 25

Removing the electrons from an atom would make the atom?

A – Positively charged.

B – A negative ion.

C – Negatively charged.

D – A positive ion.

Answer [ ]

ANSWERS TO BASICS – TEST SECTION 2

Q1. B = fuse

EXPLANATION = a fuse can be used as a safety device which will blow, i.e. melt, if the current through it exceeds a specified value. A fuse consists of a strip of wire that melts/breaks an electrical circuit when the current is deemed to be at an unsafe level.

Q2. B = sound

EXPLANATION = sound is not an effect of electrical current.

Q3. C = the refuelling tank and the aeroplane itself are earthed

EXPLANATION = when a tank of an aeroplane is being refuelled, the refuelling tank and the aeroplane are earthed. A bonding line is used to earth the aeroplane before it is refuelled, in order to ensure that it is safe to add fuel to the aircraft's tank.

Q4. B = the ammeter needs to be connected in series

EXPLANATION = in order to measure the current of the circuit, which is measured using a device called an ammeter, the ammeter needs to be positioned within a series circuit.

Q5. D = 10,000 volts

EXPLANATION = a 'kilo' is equivalent to 1,000. So 10 kilovolts is equivalent to 10,000 volts.

Q6. A = E = I × V × T

EXPLANATION = in order to calculate the energy transferred, you would need to use the following equation:
$E = I \times V \times T$.

Q7. D = 80,000J

EXPLANATION = in order to calculate the energy in this question, you will need to use the following equation = I × V × T. So, 20 × 16 × 250 = 80,000J Remember, energy is measured in Joules, so you need to make sure that you have used the correct units.

Q8. D = bulbs 1 and 2 will illuminate

EXPLANATION = if the switch is closed, and bulb 3 is removed from the circuit, that means only bulbs 1 and 2 will illuminate. Bulb 4 will not illuminate because the removal of bulb 3 breaks the path of wiring and therefore prevents bulb 4 from lighting up. The removal of bulb 3 is on a different path to bulbs and 1 and 2, and therefore does not affect them from illuminating.

Q9. Ohmmeter

EXPLANATION = the symbol represents an ohmmeter.

Q10. C = other components keep working even if one fails

EXPLANATION = the useful thing about parallel circuits is that if one element of the circuit fails, it does not affect the others. For example, in a series circuit, if one bulb blows, it will stop all of the other bulbs from illuminating. Whereas, in a parallel circuit, if one bulb blows, the other bulbs will continue to work.

Q11. Circuit B

EXPLANATION = circuit B has the smallest current because the diagram contains two resistors which share the current, whereas Circuit A only contains one resistor and therefore the current is not being shared.

Q12. Thermistor

EXPLANATION = the symbol represents a thermistor.

Q13. A = used as a temperature sensor. The resistance decreases as the temperature increases

EXPLANATION = using the symbol from the previous question (the thermistor), it can best be described as a temperature sensor. The resistance decreases as the temperature increases. They act as sensitive resistors which have the primary function of changing resistance when subject to changes in temperature. At high temperatures, the resistance of a thermistor is low, and more current is able to pass through. Whereas at low temperatures, the resistance of the thermistor is high, and less current is able to pass through.

Q14. C = silver, copper, aluminium, water, PVC, rubber

EXPLANATION = metals are a conductor of electricity. Whereas, rubber and plastics are insulators of electricity. Therefore the correct order which demonstrates the best to worst conductors of electricity should be written as follows: silver, copper, aluminium, water, PVC and rubber.

Q15. B = the bulbs will become dimmer

EXPLANATION = if you swapped a thick wire with a thin wire, the bulbs in the circuit will in fact become dimmer. This is because a thin wire provides more resistance compared to a thicker wire, and therefore dims the light of the bulbs because the flow of current is being restricted.

Q16. D = they use a smaller current

EXPLANATION = LEDs, also known as light emitting diodes, are becoming increasingly used due to them using a smaller current.

Q17. A = attract

EXPLANATION = when plastic is rubbed against a cloth material, this will allow small pieces of paper to be attracted. This is because of the different electronic charges from the plastic and the cloth, which causes it to attract an object, such as paper.

Q18. B = electrons

EXPLANATION = current electricity occurs when electrons flow freely between more than one object. In electrical circuits, the charge is often carried through electrons that move through the wire. This can either be a direct current or an alternating current.

Q19. A = the pump which supplies energy to move the water around

EXPLANATION = if an electrical circuit is an analogue for a waterpark that means that the battery of a circuit is the analogue for the pump which supplies the energy for the water to move around. In a waterpark, a pump is needed to push the water around in order to supply water in all the areas of the waterpark. This is similar to what the battery does in an electrical circuit. The battery supplies the energy which moves around the circuit in order to energise the entire circuit.

Q20. D = the same as the current through the light bulb

EXPLANATION = the current through the battery is the same as the current through the light bulb. There is nothing restricting the flow of current, and the current is not shared by more than one element, therefore the current will be the same.

Q21. E = the potential difference between the bird's feet is low

EXPLANATION = a charge can only flow between the objects if an electrical potential difference has been established. If a bird places a foot on the line and then places its other foot a few centimetres away, there is little or no difference in its potential, and therefore has no charge which makes the bird landing on the line, safe.

Q22. D = remove one of the bulbs

EXPLANATION = if you removed one of the bulbs, this would increase the current in the circuit. The current would increase because removing a bulb from the circuit will decrease the resistance of the overall circuit.

Q23. C = current

EXPLANATION = a diode is a component that permits a current to flow in only one direction. Therefore, the diode regulates current.

Q24. B = farad

EXPLANATION = the SI unit of capacitance is the farad.

Q25. D = a positive ion

EXPLANATION = removing the electrons from an atom would make the atom a positive ion.

BASICS –
TEST
SECTION 3

Question 1

Which of the following does not pose a safety risk of an electrical shock?

A	B	C
A 'live' wire	A plug into a socket	A frayed wire

Answer [   ]

Question 2

Which of the following bests describes the function of a green and yellow striped wire in a plug?

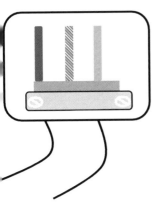

A – Completes the circuit.

B – Carries high voltage.

C – A safety wire that prevents the appliance from becoming 'live'.

Answer [   ]

Question 3

A disadvantage of series circuits is, the more components there are in a circuit, the more _ _ _ _ _ _ .

A – Current.

B – Flow.

C – Resistance.

D – Power.

E – Voltage.

Answer

Question 4

In the series circuit below, ammeter 1 (A1) shows the reading of 1.5A. What will be the reading of ammeter 2 (A2) and ammeter 3 (A3), respectively?

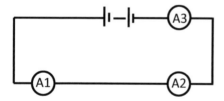

A – 1.0A and 0.5A.

B – 1.5A and 1.0A.

C – 1.0A and 1.0A.

D – 0.5A and 0.5A.

E – 1.5A and 1.5A.

Answer

Question 5

The battery shown below has an output of 4 volts. The lightbulb glows moderately. If we were to replace the 4 volt battery with a 2 volt battery, what will happen to the light?

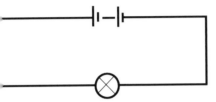

A – The lightbulb will shine more brightly.

B – The lightbulb will have the same level of brightness.

C – The lightbulb will shine more dimly.

D – The lightbulb will go out.

Answer

Question 6

The below circuit contains a 2 volts battery, a resistor of 2 Ω, and an ammeter which reads a current of 1 amp. If we replace the 2 ohm resistor with a 1 ohm resistor, what will the ammeter read?

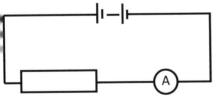

A – 1 amp.

B – 0.5 amp.

C – 2 amps.

D – 4 amps.

Answer

Question 7

Identify the following symbol:

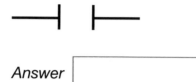

Answer

Question 8

What is the resistance in this circuit?

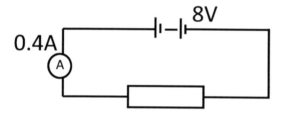

A – 0.5Ω.

B – 20Ω.

C – 0.4Ω.

D – 10Ω.

E – 0.32Ω.

Answer

Question 9

A 4.5A ammeter is connected in a circuit to a 6V battery. What is the power?

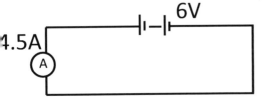

Answer [   ]

Question 10

What is the voltage if a current of 3.5A flows through a 28W lightbulb?

A – 8 volts.

B – 98 volts.

C – 4 volts.

D – 24 volts.

E – 0.15 volts.

Answer [   ]

Question 11

Calculate the total resistance in this parallel circuit.

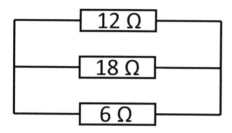

Answer

Question 12

In terms of electricity, which of the following is the odd one out?

Iron   Glass   Steel   Tin

Answer

Question 13

Using the above question, why is that answer the odd one out?

A – Because it doesn't let electricity flow through it.

B – Because it is breakable.

C – Because it is transparent.

D – Because it lets electricity flow through it.

Answer

Question 14

The lead of a pencil can conduct electricity. True or false?

Answer [   ]

Question 15

Ammeters measure the amount of current in a circuit. In the circuit below, all the ammeters are identical. If ammeter A1 reads 12A, what will ammeter A3 read?

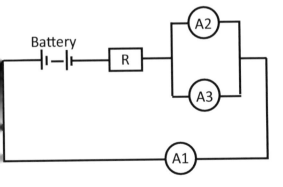

Answer [   ]

Question 16

In the following circuit, if switches A and B are closed, and bulb B is removed which bulbs will illuminate?

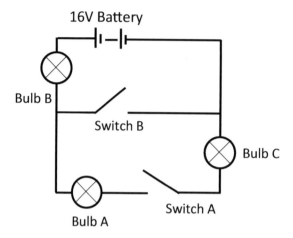

A – Bulb A only.

B – Bulb C only.

C – Bulbs A and C only.

D – No bulbs will illuminate.

Answer

Question 17

In the following circuit, how many switches need to close to light up 2 bulbs?

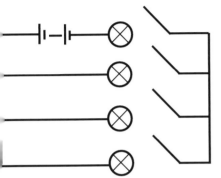

Answer

Question 18

What type of charge does an object have if it gains electrons?

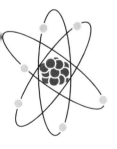

A – Positive.

B – Negative.

C – Neutral.

D – Positive or negative.

Answer

Question 19

What transfers from a carpet made from nylon to give off a static electrical shock?

A – Nucleus.

B – Protons.

C – Electrons.

D – Electricity.

E – Atoms.

Answer

Question 20

What will the voltage at point A be, if the battery is 8 volts?

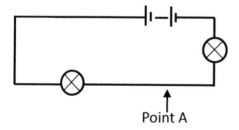

Point A

A – 8 volts.

B – 4 volts.

C – 16 volts.

D – 0.4 volts.

Answer

Question 21

One ampere or amp, is the amount of current that exists when _ _ _ _ _ _ flows through a certain point of a conductor in _ _ _ _ _ _ .

A – One coulomb; one hour.

B – One electron; one second.

C – One volt; one hour.

D – One coulomb; one second.

E – One electron; one hour.

Answer

Question 22

The charge which flows through the circuit is most energised at _ _ _ _ _ _ .

A – The '-' terminal of the battery.

B – The charge is the same throughout the circuit.

C – The '+' terminal of the battery.

D – Prior to entering the bulb.

E – Just after exiting the bulb.

Answer

Question 23

When a lightbulb is no longer working, this is likely due to...

A – Running out of electrons.

B – Being burned out.

C – A broken fuse box.

D – A broken filament.

E – All of the above.

Answer [   ]

Question 24

Using the below diagram, the resistors are connected in?

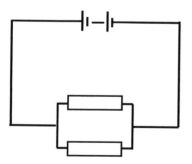

A	B	C
Series	Parallel	Cannot say

Question 25

The unit of electricity is…

A – Watt.

B – Amp.

C – Volt.

D – Current.

Answer [   ]

ANSWERS TO BASICS – TEST SECTION 3

Q1. B = a plug into a socket

EXPLANATION = putting a plug into a socket will not cause an electrical shock. The wirings of the plug are covered by plastic coating which prevents any electrical shocks from coming through. A 'live' wire like an electric fence for example, will pose the risk of an electrical shock, just as a frayed wire would. If a wire is frayed and is touched, that will cause an electric shock. The wires are open and therefore, if touched, will cause a shock.

Q2. C = a safety wire that prevents the appliance from becoming 'live'

EXPLANATION = the green and yellow striped wire, i.e. the 'earth' wire in a plug, is used as a safety wire that prevents the appliance from becoming 'live' and thus prevents an electrical shock. The blue wire is the 'neutral' wire that completes the circuit, and the brown wire is the 'live' wire that carries a high voltage within the electrical circuit.

Q3. C = resistance

EXPLANATION = a disadvantage of series circuits is the more components there are, the more resistance the current has to flow through. Each component of a circuit restricts the flow, and thus the more components, the more restriction.

Q4. E = 1.5A and 1.5A

EXPLANATION = ammeters 1, 2 and 3 all have the same reading of 1.5A. A series circuit has just one current flowing through, therefore each of the readings for each ammeter will be the same.

Q5. C = the lightbulb will shine more dimly

EXPLANATION = if we replaced a 4 volt battery with a 2 volt battery, this means that the lightbulb in the circuit will shine more dimly. This is because a 2 volt battery only provides half as much energy as the 4 volt battery. Therefore, the lamp will convert less heat and light because there is not as much energy passing through the circuit as before.

Q6. C = 2 amps

EXPLANATION = a 1 amp resistor is half of a 2 amp resistor. This means that it is twice as easy for the current to flow through the circuit. Using Ohm's law = V = IR. To solve I = V ÷ R, 2 ÷ 1 = 2.

Q7. Capacitor

EXPLANATION = the symbol represents a capacitor. A capacitor stores the electrical charge of the circuit. It can be used alongside a resistor in a 'timing' circuit. It can be used to act as a sort of 'filter', whereby it blocks direct current (DC) signals from running through the circuit, but permits alternating current (AC) signals to do so.

Q8. B = 20Ω

EXPLANATION = in order to work out the resistance, you need to use the following equation: resistance = voltage ÷ current = 8 ÷ 0.4 = 20Ω.

Q9. 27 watts

EXPLANATION = in order to work out the power, you need to use the following equation: power = voltage × current = 6 × 4.5 = 27 watts.

Q10. A = 8 volts

EXPLANATION = in order to work out the voltage, you need to use the following equation: voltage = power ÷ current = 28 ÷ 3.5 = 8.

Q11. 3.27Ω

EXPLANATION = in order to work out total resistance of the circuit, you need to follow these steps:

Step 1 = R1 + R2 + R3 = 12 + 18 + 6 = 36.

Step 2 = using 36 as the bottom part of the fraction, you need to work ou[t] what each resistance is needed to multiply, in order to get the same numbe[r] for the bottom number.

$$1/12 = 3/12 = (12 \times 3 = 36).$$

$$1/18 = 2/36 \; (12 \times 2 = 36) \quad 1/6 = 6/36 (6 \times 6 = 36).$$

Step 3 $= 11/36 = 36 \div 11 = 3.27\Omega.$

Q12. Glass

EXPLANATION = glass is the odd one out because all of the other materials are types of metals.

Q13. A = because it doesn't let electricity flow through it

EXPLANATION = glass is the odd one out because the other materials are types of metals and let electricity flow. Whereas, glass does not let electricity flow.

Q14. True

EXPLANATION = the lead of a pencil does conduct electricity. Despite the lead in a pencil being made from granite, it is one of the few non-metallic materials that can conduct electricity reasonably well.

Q15. 6 amps

EXPLANATION = if ammeter A1 reads 12A, then ammeters A2 and A3 will have to share this current, therefore each of these would read 6.

Q16. D = no bulbs will illuminate

EXPLANATION = if you removed bulb B from the circuit, no other bulbs would illuminate, even after closing the switches. If bulb B is removed, it will affect the path of the circuit. The bulbs are positioned on the same path and therefore, if one bulb goes, the others will not work.

Q17. Two

EXPLANATION = two switches need to close in order to light up two lightbulbs. Two lightbulbs are connected in one path of wiring, therefore two switches will need to close, in order to light up two bulbs.

Q18. B = negative

EXPLANATION = electrons have a negative charge and so objects that gain them, have a negative charge overall.

Q19. C = electrons

EXPLANATION = electrons are transferred from a nylon carpet to give off a static electrical shock. Protons remain in the nucleus and cannot be transferred.

Q20. A = 8 volts

EXPLANATION = in a series circuit, there is only one path for the current, and therefore that current is the same at all of the points of the path.

Q21. D = one coulomb; one second

EXPLANATION = an ampere is the unit which measures electrical current. Electrical current is the rate at which the charge of a circuit moves past a certain point which is measured in coulombs of charge per second.

Q22. C = the '+' terminal of the battery

EXPLANATION = the '+' terminal of the battery is the part of the circuit that is most energised.

Q23. D = a broken filament

EXPLANATION = the most common cause for a lightbulb to not be working is because the filament in the bulb is broken. This is the coiled wire and if it overheats or is overused, it is likely to blow, resulting in the lightbulb being ineffective.

Q24. B = parallel

EXPLANATION = the two resistors in the circuit are connected in paralle In a circuit, if a path of wiring comes to a junction, i.e. more than one pat can be taken, this means that the circuit is parallel. You should notice tha the diagram contains a junction and therefore the resistors are positioned in parallel to one another.

Q25. C = volt

EXPLANATION = the unit of electricity is volt (V).

BASICS –
TEST
SECTION 4

Question 1

Which electrical component is the following a description of?

A component that allows the current to flow only in one direction.

A – Resistor.

B – Capacitor.

C – Diode.

D – Conductors.

E – Thermistor.

Answer

Question 2

What happens when opposite charges move towards each other?

A	B	C
They attract	They repel	They waver

Question 3

What happens when like charges move towards each other?

A	B	C
They attract	They repel	They waver

Question 4

When a cloth is rubbed against an object made of copper, no charge happens because...

A – Copper is a conductor.

B – Copper is an insulator.

C – The cloth is not electronically charged.

D – It is a brittle metal.

Answer [   ]

Question 5

If electricity costs 8p per unit and a 6 kW appliance runs for approximately 75 minutes, what is the total cost?

A – £3600.

B – £9.80.

C – £48.00.

D – £36.00.

E – £3.60.

Answer [   ]

Question 6

Which switch or switches, need to be closed in order for bulb B to light up?

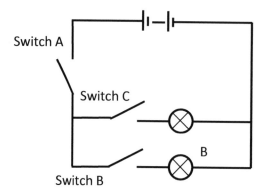

A – Switch A.

B – Switches A and C.

C – Switch C.

D – Switches A and B.

E – All of the switches.

Answer

Question 7

The flow of current in a circuit can _ _ _ _ _ _ when a component is not working.

A – Decrease.

B – Increase.

C – Increase or decrease.

D – Stay the same.

Answer

Question 8

What is the reading on the ammeter, A1, in the circuit below?

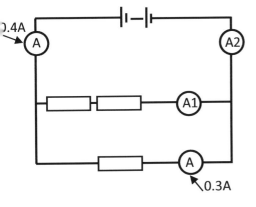

A	B	C	D
0.4A	0.3A	0.1A	0.7A

Question 9

Which electrical component is the following a description of?

As light intensity increases, the resistance goes down.

A – Light emitting diode.

B – Variable resistor.

C – Thermistor.

D – Light dependent resistor.

E – Voltmeter.

Answer

Question 10

Draw the symbol for a light emitting diode.

Question 11

The potential difference across each branch within a parallel circuit is _ _ _ _ _ _ as the potential difference across the source.

A – Lower.

B – Higher.

C – The same.

D – Fluctuate.

Answer

Question 12

Material that loses _ _ _ _ _ _ becomes negatively charged.

A – Atoms.

B – Neutrons.

C – Particles.

D – Electrons.

Answer

Question 13

Using the diagrams below, which ammeter (A1, A2 or A3) has the smallest current?

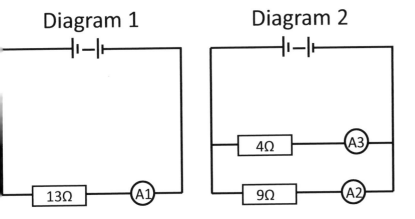

Diagram 1

Diagram 2

A	B	C
A1	A2	A3

Answer

Question 14

Using the circuit below, what would the voltage be across the 10 ohm resistor?

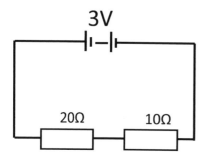

A – 2V.

B – 1V.

C – 4V.

D – 10V.

Answer

Question 15

What is the resistance of an electrical component if the voltage across it is 18V, and the current of 3A flows through it?

A – 54 ohms.

B – 3 ohms.

C – 6 ohms.

D – 18 ohms.

E – None of the above.

Answer

Question 16

Which of the following equations would you use to work out the voltage?

A – Voltage = current ÷ resistance.

B – Voltage = resistance ÷ current.

C – Voltage = current × resistance.

D – Voltage = power × resistance.

Answer [   ]

Question 17

Draw a diagram that illustrates where a voltmeter should be placed in a circuit in order to measure the voltage.

Question 18

The flow of current through each lightbulb in a circuit is _ _ _ _ _ _ when there are _ _ _ _ _ _ lamps.

A – Less; less.

B – Less; more.

C – More; more.

D – Cannot say.

Answer [   ]

Question 19

Place the following words in the correct column of the table to distinguish the insulators from the conductors.

Oxygen   Rock   Brass   Solder   Graphite   Plastic   Wood
Diamond   Salt Solution   Platinum   Water   Rubber   Glass
Porcelain   Silver   Human Body   Paper   Styrofoam

Conductors	Insulators

Question 20

When an oil tanker arrives at its destination, it empties the fuel into either a reservoir or tank. In order to do this, the oil tank is often connected with a metal wire into the ground. Out of the following, which of the answers below provides the best reasoning for this?

A – To provide more support.

B – To move the electrons from the tank into the ground.

C – To ease the transition from one tank to another.

D – To transfer the static charge that builds up to the ground, to prevent an ignition of fuel.

Answer

Question 21

Which of the following best describes why your hair sticks up after rubbing a balloon on your head?

A – Rubbing two conducted materials together makes it electronically charged. The electrons move from one object to another, causing static electricity.

B – Rubbing two insulated materials together makes it electronically charged. The protons move from one object to another, causing static electricity.

C – Rubbing two insulated materials together makes it electronically charged. The electrons move from one object to another, causing static electricity.

D – Rubbing two conducted materials together makes it electronically charged. The protons move from one object to another, causing static electricity.

Answer

Question 22

Which electrical component is the following a description of?

A subatomic particle that carries the smallest of magnitudes of negative electricity.

A – Protons.

B – Nucleus.

C – Atoms.

D – Electrons.

Answer

Question 23

Which electrical component is the following a description of?

An output device which includes a coil of wire that subsequently creates a magnetic field when a current passes through.

A – Conductor.

B – Thermistor.

C – Inductor.

D – Resistor.

Answer

Question 24

What is the current in the circuit below?

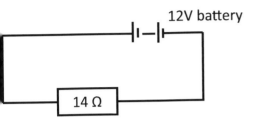

A – 0.85A.

B – 2A.

C – 12A.

D – 14A.

Answer

Question 25

An atom is _ _ _ _ _ _ .

A – Positively charged.

B – Negatively charged.

C – Electronically neutral.

D – Any of the above.

Answer

ANSWERS TO BASICS – TEST SECTION 4

Q1. C = diode

EXPLANATION = a diode is an electrical component that allows the current to flow only in one direction.

Q2. A = they attract

EXPLANATION = when opposite charges come together, they attract. If one object is charged, and the other is not; they will attract.

Q3. B = they repel

EXPLANATION = when like charges come together, they repel. If both objects are charged, they will repel.

Q4. A = copper is a conductor

EXPLANATION = copper is a material that is a conductor, and therefore does not permit any electrical charge.

Q5. D = £36.00

EXPLANATION = in order to work out the cost, you will need to use the following equation: power × time × cost per unit = 6 × 75 × 8 = 3600p, or £36.00.

Q6. D = switches A and B

EXPLANATION = in order for lightbulb B to illuminate, switch A and B need to be closed. Switch A and B is on the same path of wiring as lightbulb B, therefore you would need both of these switches to be closed to light up the bulb.

Q7. B = increase

EXPLANATION = the flowing current through a circuit can dramatically increase if a component stops working. If a component stops working, that means there is less resistance for the current to flow through.

Q8. C = 0.1A

EXPLANATION = 0.4 = 0.3 + A1, so A1 would be 0.1 (0.1 + 0.3 = 0.4).

Q9. D = light dependent resistor

EXPLANATION = the definition of a light dependent resistor is 'as light intensity increases, the resistance goes down'. Therefore, the correct answer is answer option D.

Q10. The light emitting diode should look something like this:

Q11. C = the same

EXPLANATION = the potential difference across each branch within a parallel circuit is the same as the potential difference across the source.

Q12. D = electrons

EXPLANATION = material that loses electrons becomes negatively charged. Electrons create a negative charge that balances the positive charge of the protons.

Q13. A = A1

EXPLANATION = Ammeter A1 would read the smallest current. This is because A1 has the largest resistance, and therefore restricts the flow of current moving through the circuit.

Q14. B = 1V

EXPLANATION = the 10 ohm resistor will read 1V. This is because the other resistor is 2V and the overall circuit is 3V, therefore the resistor will read 1V.

Q15. C = 6 ohms

EXPLANATION = in order to work out the resistance, you will need to use the following equation: resistance = voltage ÷ current. So, 18 ÷ 3 = 6 ohms.

Q16. C = voltage = current × resistance

EXPLANATION = in order to work out the voltage, you must multiply the current of the circuit by the resistance.

Q17. The circuit showing a voltmeter in the correct position for measuring the voltage, should look something like this:

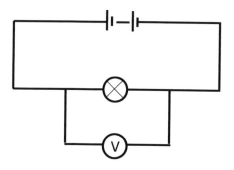

Q18. B = less; more

EXPLANATION = the current flow through each lightbulb is less when there are more bulbs. The more bulbs, the more resistance and therefore the less current that flows through.

Q19. Below illustrates where each word should be placed in the table:

Conductors: brass, solder, graphite, salt solution, platinum, water, silver, human body.

Insulators: oxygen, rock, plastic, wood, diamond, rubber, glass, porcelain, paper, styrofoam.

Q20. D = to transfer the static charge that builds up to the ground, to prevent an ignition of fuel

EXPLANATION = when an oil tanker is being unfuelled, a wire is placed into the ground so that the static charge that builds up from the object, does not cause a safety hazard. Instead the charge is transferred to the ground, preventing the oil from igniting.

Q21. C = rubbing two insulated materials together makes is electronically charged. The electrons move from one object to another, causing static electricity

EXPLANATION = this is the best description of why rubbing a balloon on your head causes your hair to stick up. The two insulated objects become electronically charged, and when the electrons move from one object to another, it causes static electricity between both objects.

Q22. D = electrons

EXPLANATION = electrons are a subatomic particle that carries the smallest of magnitudes of negative electricity.

Q23. C = inductor

EXPLANATION = an inductor is an output device which includes a coil of wire that subsequently creates a magnetic field when a current passes through.

Q24. A = 0.85A

EXPLANATION = in order to work out the current, you need to use the following equation: current = voltage $\div$ resistance = 12 $\div$ 14 = 0.85.

Q25. C = electronically neutral

EXPLANATION = an atom is electronically neutral. They do not have an overall electrical charge.

ADVANCED
ELECTRICAL
COMPREHENSION

In this section of the guide, we have provided you with testing questions that are specifically designed to aid you through advanced levels of electrical comprehension.

In this section, we have focused on the following areas:

- Series and Parallel Circuits;
- Transformers;
- Monitoring and Measuring Alternating and Direct Currents;
- Voltages;
- Tolerable Resistances;
- Impedances;
- Magnetic Fields;
- Wheatstone Bridge Circuit;
- Earth-Fault Loops;
- Eddy Currents;
- Potential Difference;
- Capacitances;
- Residual Current Monitoring Device (RCM);
- Resistors;
- Diodes.

Before you begin the testing sections, take a look at the following example pages of **advanced** Electrical Comprehension. The examples include useful information regarding the questions you will encounter, how to work out the questions, the representation of symbols, and provide insightful advice and tips on how to answer the questions successfully.

EXAMPLES OF ADVANCED ELECTRICAL COMPREHENSION

CIRCUIT SYMBOLS

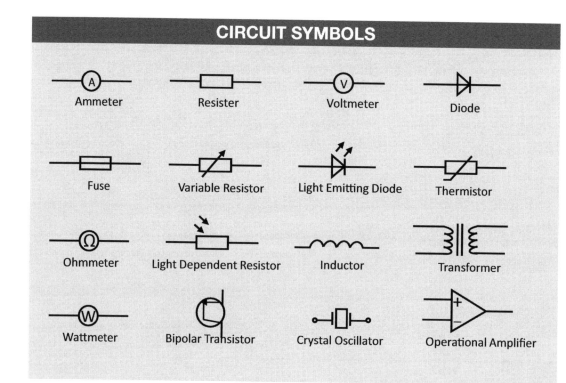

GLOSSARY

- **Ammeter**: an ammeter is an electrical unit that measures current.

- **Analogue electronics**: systems with a continuous variable signal.

- **Capacitor**: a capacitor stores the electrical charge of the circuit. It can be used alongside a resistor in a 'timing' circuit. It can be used to act as a sort of 'filter', whereby it blocks direct current (DC) signals, but permits alternating current (AC) signals running through the circuit.

- **Conductor**: an electrical conductor is anything or any material which can carry an electrical current. Other conductors may conduct heat.

- **Diode:** a diode is an electrical device that only permits current flow in one direction.

- **Dual element fuse:** a fuse that contains a metal strip that melts instantly on a short circuit.

- **Eddy currents:** a current in a conducting material which results in induction by moving or varying the magnetic field.

- **Electromagnets:** the relationship between electric fields and magnetic fields.

- **Electron:** a subatomic particle that carries the smallest of magnitudes of negative electricity.

- **Fuse:** a fuse acts as a 'safety device' for electrical circuits. The fuse will blow, i.e. melt, if the current flowing through the circuit exceeds a specified value.

- **Impedance:** the ratio of the voltage to the current within an alternating current.

- **Inductor:** an inductor is an output device which includes a coil of wire that subsequently creates a magnetic field when a current passes through. It can often be used as a transducer to convert electrical energy into mechanical energy by this idea of 'pulling on something'.

- **Insulator:** an insulator is a material which acts as a very poor conductor of electricity. Electrical wires are often covered with an insulating material in order to guard the circuit's electrical supply and provide a safety precaution for people using them.

- **Internal resistance:** all electric materials have some resistance. This resistance is called internal resistance.

- **Light dependent resistor:** a light dependent resistor, or a photoresistor, is a light-controlled variable. They change resistance as the light level changes.

- **Light emitting diode:** often abbreviated as LED, light emitting diode is a transducer which converts energy into light.

- **Ohmmeter:** ohmmeter is a device that measures resistance.

- **Ohm's law:** ohm's law states that the current in a circuit between two points is directly proportional to the voltage and inversely proportional to resistance.

- **Resistor:** a resistor is a term that is self-explanatory. It restricts the flow of current. For example, a resistor can be used to restrict the flow of current in an LED.

- **Root mean square voltages:** this refers to the mathematical way to define the effective voltage or current in an alternating current.

- **Transformer:** a transformer is a type of power supply. It contains two coils of wiring which are linked by an iron core. It is used to increase or decrease alternating current (AC) voltages. The transformer transfers energy through magnetic fields, not electrical fields.

- **Variable resistor:** a variable resistor is used to control the current flow. This type of resistor contains two contacts. The resistor permits the control of adjusting lamp brightness and motoring speed.

- **Voltmeter:** a voltmeter is an electrical unit that measures voltage. This is also known as *'potential difference'.*

- **Wheatstone bridge circuit:** a circuit for measuring the unknown resistance which forms a quadrilateral with three known resistors, to find out the remaining resistance.

OHM's LAW

Ohm's law is often used to analyse the electrical components within a circuit. In simple terms, Ohm's law specifically focuses on three electrical concepts:

- Potential difference (voltage);
- Current;
- Resistance.

The resistance of an electrical outlet can be found by measuring the current flow and the potential difference, i.e. the voltage running through it.

There is a simple equation to use in order to work out the relationship between current, resistance and potential difference.

REMEMBER: the following equation:

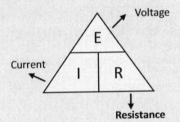

To work out the **resistance,** eliminate the 'R' from the equation:

$$R = \frac{E}{I}$$

To work out the **current,** eliminate the 'I' from the equation:

$$I = \frac{E}{R}$$

To work out the **voltage,** eliminate the 'E' from the equation:

$$E = I \times R$$

RESISTANCE TOLERABLE

In order to work out the minimum and maximum resistance tolerable of a resistor, you would need to use the following method:

EXAMPLE

What are the minimum and maximum acceptable values if a resistor has the resistance of 20 kΩ and can tolerate ±20%?

Minimum value

Step 1 – 20,000 ÷ 100 x 20 = 4,000.

Step 2 – 20,000 – 4,000 = 16,000Ω or 16 kΩ

Maximum value

Step 1 – 20,000 ÷ 100 x 20 = 4,000.

Step 2 – 20,000 + 4,000 = 24,000Ω or 24 kΩ

ELECTRICAL CALCULATIONS

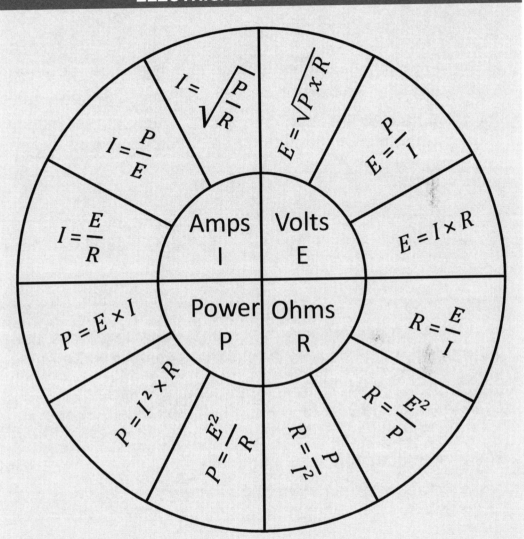

CURRENTS

AC Electricity

Alternating currents (AC) can be defined through the changes in direction in which the flow of electricity undertakes.

The UK mains supply is approximately 230V, and has a frequency of 50Hz, which is equivalent to 50 changes in direction, per second.

DC Electricity

Direct currents (DC) can be established if the current flows in one direction. For example, batteries and solar cells supply direct currents, with a typical battery supplying 1.5V.

Eddy Currents

Eddy currents is a term that was given the name because it resembled the 'eddies' in a stream. Eddies in a stream are when spirals form in the water. These spirals are often formed in a tornado-looking shape. When a current is induced in a conductor material, the induced current will flow in circles. This flow is strongest at the surface of the material.

Electromagnetism

Within electromagnetism, current also flows. The electrical term Ampere's Law illustrates how magnetic fields are powered by electrical currents.

A current is the rate of flow, otherwise known as an **electrical charge**. No current is able to flow through the circuit if it is broken. For example, if a switch is open, this prevents an electrical charge from flowing. These currents flow when **electrons** move through a conductor i.e. a metal wire.

VOLTAGES

Voltage is also known as the **potential difference or electromotive force (e.m.f.)**. The potential difference is needed to make an electrical current flow through an electrical component. For example, cells and batteries are often used to provide the potential difference needed in a circuit.

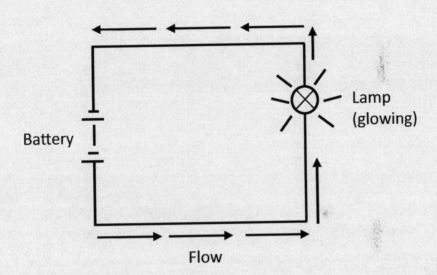

In the above electrical circuit, you will notice that there is only one source of potential difference (the battery). There is also only one source of resistance (the lamp).

Voltage Drop

This can be defined by how much voltage loss occurs through part of a circuit due to impedance. **Impedance** measures the opposition of a circuit which permits a current when voltages are applied.

Electromotive Force

Electromotive force, or e.m.f., is the voltage which is generated by a battery or magnetic field.

RESISTANCE

The term resistance refers to an electrical element that measures its opposition to a current. A resistance to the flow of electricity in a circuit occurs in most conductors.

The resistance of a wire can be increased in two ways:

- Increasing the length of the wire;
- Decreasing the thickness of the wire.

The resistance of a **long** wire is greater than the resistance of a **short** wire. This is because the electrons collide more with ions as it passes through.

The resistance in a **thin** wire is greater than that of the resistance of a **thick** wire. This is because a thin wire has fewer electrons to carry the current flow.

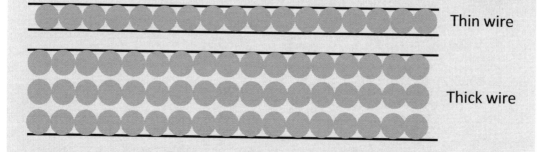

Thin wire

Thick wire

CAPACITANCE

A capacitor is an electrical component that stores charge. It has the unit of (f), meaning farads. The component consists of two plates which are separated by an insulating material.

In order to work out the capacitance of a capacitor, you should use the following method:

Capacitance = charge stored across plates ÷ potential difference across plates.

1 farad capacitor charged with 1 coulomb has the potential difference of 1 volt.

When a capacitor is fully charged, there is potential difference. The larger the area of the plates or the smaller the distance between each plate, the greater the capacitance will be.

ADVANCED –
TEST
SECTION 1

Question 1

John turns on his electrical heater. The electrical heater uses a supply of 310 volts, and the current is 11A. John wants to work out the resistance of his electrical heater. Calculate the resistance of the electrical heater. Rounded to two decimal places.

Answer

Question 2

Within a series circuit, two resistors are used. One of the resistors is 60Ω and the other is 80Ω. The voltage across the circuit is 260. What is the current of the circuit? Rounded to two decimal places.

Answer

Question 3

What are the minimum and maximum acceptable values if a resistor has the resistance of 14 kΩ and can tolerate ±20%?

Minimum value =

Maximum value =

Question 4

What is the total resistance of the network circuit below?

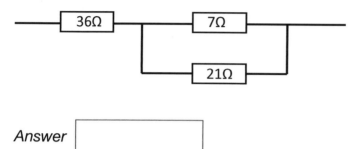

Answer

Question 5

The opposite of a current flow in an alternating current resistive circuit is...

A – Resistance.

B – Impedance.

C – Reactance.

D – Inductance.

Answer

Question 6

A resistance of 5 ohms is connected in a series circuit, with a parallel of four resistances. Each of these components is 1 ohm. What would be the equivalent resistance of the series circuit?

Answer

Question 7

_ _ _ _ _ _ are a form of wasteful circulation currents which are observed in iron cores, which result in loss of energy.

A – Core currents.

B – Hysteresis currents.

C – Neutral currents.

D – Eddy currents.

Answer

Question 8

In a circuit, the power being supplied to capacitive components, means that the voltage waveform will lag behind the current waveform. True or false?

Answer

Question 9

Explain the difference between the 'prospective short circuit current' and an 'overload current'.

Question 10

The total current flowing through the circuit below is...

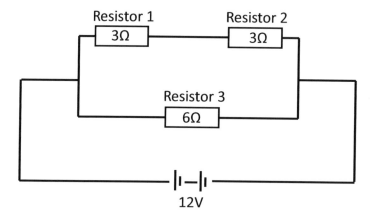

Answer

Question 11

Which of the following words best describes the explanation:

The opposite to current flow found in an alternating current circuit and is often labelled with the symbol 'Z'.

A – Inertial force.

B – Work done.

C – Impedance.

D – Step up transformers.

Answer

Question 12

On electrical equipment, where should the following symbol be included?

A – When earth bonding is not present in an electrical appliance.

B – When electrical appliances should not be exposed.

C – When electrical equipment has no insulation.

D – When electrical equipment has basic insulation only.

Answer

Question 13

Which of the following explanations best describes the function of an RCD (residual current device)?

A – A flow of electricity along an unintended path in the circuit.

B – A safety device that stops electricity passing through if there is a fault.

C – A point in a wiring system where devices can be connected.

D – A way to measure the current flowing through alternating current circuits.

Answer

Question 14

Using the component mentioned in Question 13 above, name **two** electrical appliances where RCDs would be used?

Answer [   ]

Question 15

In the diagram below, a room has two entrances. The main lighting circuit in this room would most probably be what type of switch control.

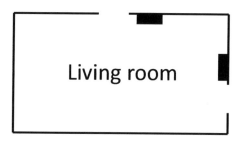

Living room

Answer [   ]

Question 16

A current of 16.5A passed through a circuit in 3 minutes. What is the quantity of electricity that is transferred?

A – 2970C.

B – 10.9C.

C – 990C.

D – 2340C.

Answer [   ]

Question 17

Calculate the total resistance of three parallel-connected resistors of 4Ω, 8Ω and 40Ω. Use the box below to show your workings out.

Answer ⬚ Ω

Question 18

In the circuit below, you will see two sets of parallel resistors. The first set of resistors are 3Ω and 30Ω in parallel with one another. The second set of resistors consists of three resistors of 9Ω, 9Ω and 9Ω.

Work out the total resistance of the circuit, if the battery connected is powered by 9V.

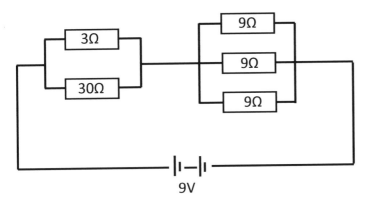

Answer ⬚

Question 19

Which of the following devices converts alternating current supply to direct current supply?

A – Inverters.

B – Choppers.

C – Rectifiers.

D – Cannot be done.

Answer

Question 20

A battery with an electromotive force of 4V produces a current of 6A around a circuit for 4 minutes. How much energy is provided in the circuit within this given time?

A	B	C	D
6570J	560J	670J	5760J

Question 21

What would happen if a copper conductor was moved across a magnetic field?

A – The wire would become magnetic.

B – A current would be induced into the wire.

C – The conductor would remain unaffected.

D – A voltage would be induced into the wire.

Answer

Question 22

What is one of the differences between electromagnets and bar magnets?

A – Electromagnets need electricity, but bar magnets do not.
B – Bar magnets have a magnetic field, but electromagnets do not.
C – Bar magnets need electricity, but electromagnets do not.
D – Electromagnets have a magnetic field, but bar magnets do not.

Answer

Question 23

What is the total resistance in the following circuit?

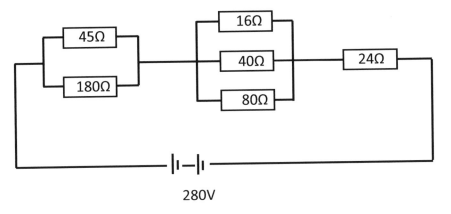

280V

Answer

Question 24

Using the diagram in Question 23, work out the current of the circuit.

Answer [   ]

Question 25

Which of the following equations demonstrates the energy stored in a capacitor?

A – E = Q × V.

B – E = ½QV.

C – E = V ÷ Q.

Answer [   ]

ANSWERS TO ADVANCED – TEST SECTION 1

Q1. 28.18Ω

EXPLANATION = in order to work out the resistance, you would need to use the following equation: Resistance = voltage ÷ current = 310 ÷ 11 = 28.1818. To two decimal placed = 28.18Ω.

Q2. 1.86A

EXPLANATION = to work out the current, you first need to add up the total of both resistors = 60 + 80 = 140. You then need to divide the voltage by the resistance of the circuit. So, 260 ÷ 140 = 1.8571. To two decimal places = 1.86A.

Q3. Minimum = 11.2 kΩ, Maximum = 16.8 kΩ

EXPLANATION = 20% of 14 kΩ, or 14,000Ω.

Step 1 = 14,000 ÷ 100 x 20 = 2,800.

Step 2 = Minimum = 14,000 – 2,800 = 11,200Ω, or 11.2 kΩ.

Step 3 = Maximum = 14,000 + 2,800 = 16,800Ω or 16.8 kΩ.

Q4. 41.25Ω

EXPLANATION = in order to work out the total resistance of the circuit, you should use the following method:

Step 1 $= \dfrac{1}{7} + \dfrac{1}{21} = \dfrac{3+1}{21} = \dfrac{4}{21}$

Step 2 = So, 21 ÷ 4 = 5.25.

Step 3 = 5.25 + 36 = 41.25Ω.

Q5. A = resistance

EXPLANATION = the definition of the opposite of a current flow in an alternating current restrictive circuit is resistance.

Q6. 5.25 ohms

EXPLANATION = the circuit is a 5 ohms series, which contains four components of 1 ohm each. Each of the components must be 0.25 (0.25 × 4 = 1 ohm). Therefore 5 ohms + 0.25 = 5.25 ohms.

Q7. D = eddy currents

EXPLANATION = Eddy currents lose energy due to the changes in magnetic fields in a conductor or core.

Q8. True

EXPLANATION = in capacitor circuits, the voltage waveform will lag behind the current waveform. Whereas in inductive circuits, this would be the exact opposite.

Q9. Your answer should read something like this:

An 'overload' current is an overcurrent which occurs in a circuit that is electronically sound. In other words, it is carrying more current than it was originally designed to carry. This is usually because of a fault in the circuit, or too many components connected within the circuit. The 'prospective short circuit current' is the maximum current that the transformer is able to deliver.

Q10. 4A

EXPLANATION = in order to work out the total current, you should use the following equations:

$$\frac{1}{R} = \frac{1}{R1+2} + \frac{1}{R3} = \frac{1}{6} + \frac{1}{6} = \frac{2}{6}$$

So, $6 \div 2 = 3$

$12V \div 3 = 4A$.

Q11. C = impedance

EXPLANATION = impedance is the total opposite of the current flow in an alternating current circuit, and is labelled Z. An impedance is a way to measure the ratio between the voltage and the current in an alternating current circuit.

Q12. D = when electrical equipment has basic insulation only

EXPLANATION = the symbol is used on electrical equipment to indicate that it has basic insulation only.

Q13. B = a safety device that stops electricity passing through if there is a fault

EXPLANATION = an RCD (residual current device) is a safety device that stops electricity passing through if there is a fault.

Q14. Kitchen appliances, cord extension leads, bathroom appliances, hand-held appliances, power tools, garden appliances

EXPLANATION = the list above illustrates some of the examples whereby an RCD would be used to prevent any hazards. Lawn mowers, hair dryers, drills, curling wands, electric jack-hammers etc. This list is not exhaustive and so if your answer does not fit in to any of the above categories, research it online.

Q15. Two-way switch control

EXPLANATION = if a room has two entrances, it is more than likely that the room will operate a two-way switch control. In simpler terms, a switch may be positioned at each entrance to the room, and therefore if the room has two entrances, two switches will most likely be used.

Q16. A = 2970 C

EXPLANATION = in order to work out the electricity transferred, you should use the following method:

$16.5 \times 3 \times 60 = 2970$ C.

Q17. 2.5Ω

EXPLANATION = in order to work out the total resistance, use the following equation:

$$\frac{1}{R} = \frac{1}{R1} + \frac{1}{R2} + \frac{1}{R3}$$

$$\frac{1}{4} + \frac{1}{8} + \frac{1}{40} = \frac{10+5+1}{40} = \frac{16}{40}$$

So, 40 ÷ 16 = 2.5Ω.

Q18. 5.72Ω

EXPLANATION = in order to work out the total resistance in the circuit, use the following method:

Step 1 = first you should work out the first set of resistors:

$$\frac{1}{3} + \frac{1}{30} = \frac{10+1}{30} = \frac{11}{30}$$

So, 30 ÷ 11 = 2.72.

Step 2 = now work out the second set of resistors:

$$\frac{1}{9} + \frac{1}{9} + \frac{1}{9} = \frac{3}{9}$$

So, 9 ÷ 3 = 3.

Step 3 = to work out the total resistance, add both of these up = 2.72 + 3 = 5.72Ω.

Q19. C = rectifiers

EXPLANATION = rectification is the process which converts alternating current supply into direct current supply. It works by permitting only some or no current through in the opposite direction of the flowing current.

Q20. D = 5760J

EXPLANATION = in order to work out how much energy is transferred, you should use the following equation:

Total charge transferred/charge = current × time.

So, 6 × 4 × 60 = 1440.

(volts × coulomb) = 4 × 1440 = 5760J.

Q21. D = a voltage would be instigated into the wire

EXPLANATION = a voltage can be induced into the wire if the copper conductor is moved across a magnetic field. Some of the electrons are free and therefore contain a force. The electrons are pushed downwards which leaves behind a positive charge. The electrons are negatively charged, so the charge in the wire has become separated which causes a voltage.

Q22. A = electromagnets need electricity, but bar magnets do not

EXPLANATION = (electro)magnets are quite self-explanatory. They need electricity in order to work. Whereas bar magnets do not require electricity to work.

Q23. 70Ω

EXPLANATION = in order to work out the total resistance of the circuit, you should use the following method:

$$\text{Step 1} = \frac{1}{45} + \frac{1}{180} = \frac{4+1}{180} = \frac{5}{180}$$

So, 180 ÷ 5 = 36.

$$\text{Step 2} = \frac{1}{16} + \frac{1}{40} + \frac{1}{80} = \frac{5+2+1}{80} = \frac{8}{80}$$

So, 80 ÷ 8 = 10.

$$\text{Step 3} = \frac{1}{24} = 24.$$

Step 4 = 36 + 10 + 24 = 70Ω.

Q24. 4A

EXPLANATION = in order to work out the current, you will need to use your answer from the previous question to help you work out the answer for this question.

Total resistance = 70Ω.

Total volts = 280V.

So, 280 ÷ 70 = 4A.

Q25. B = E = ½QV

EXPLANATION = in order to work out the energy stored in a capacitor, you would need to use the following equation:

$E = ½QV$ = energy = ½ charge × volt.

ADVANCED –
TEST
SECTION 2

Question 1

Using the Wheatstone bridge circuit below, calculate the resistance of R3.

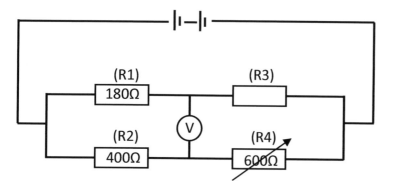

Answer [   ]

Question 2

What is the effective capacitance of the following circuit?

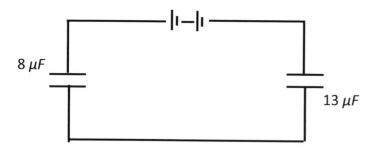

A – 17 µF.

B – 5 µF.

C – 8 µF.

D – 21 µF.

Answer [   ]

Question 3

A battery has an e.m.f. reading of 4V, and an internal resistance of 2.6. The circuit comprises a battery, a variable resistor, an ammeter and a voltmeter.

Mark wants to decrease the resistance of the variable resistor. What will happen to the voltmeter and the ammeter once Mark decreases the resistance of the variable resistor?

A – The ammeter reading will increase; the voltmeter reading will decrease.

B – The ammeter reading will decrease; the voltmeter reading will increase.

C – The ammeter reading will stay the same; the voltmeter reading will decrease.

D – The ammeter reading will increase; the voltmeter reading will increase.

Answer

Question 4

Harrison is an electrician. He cuts a hole through a steel plate. He does this twice. Once using a hand drill, and the other using an electrical drill. He is trying to decide which drill to continue using on the steel plate. Explain, using the concept of *work done* and *power*, why the electrical drill is the best tool for the job.

Question 5

The Wheatstone bridge circuit below is balanced, with R2 = 40Ω, R3 = 20Ω and R4 = 80Ω. What is the value or R1?

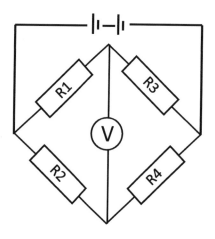

A	B	C	D
5Ω	20Ω	10Ω	40Ω

Question 6

Michael buys a battery to power an electrical toy for his son Adam. The battery has a potential difference which is measured to be 1.65V. This is the potential difference when the toy is not turned on. When the toy is turned on, the potential difference of the battery is 1.58V. This produces a current of 0.55.

Which of the following terms best describes the cause of the drop in potential difference of the toy?

A – Electromotive force.

B – Reduced resistance.

C – Increased current flow.

D – Internal resistance.

Answer

Question 7

Below is a graph illustrating the terminal potential difference of the current of a battery. Use the graph to work out what the internal resistance of the battery would be.

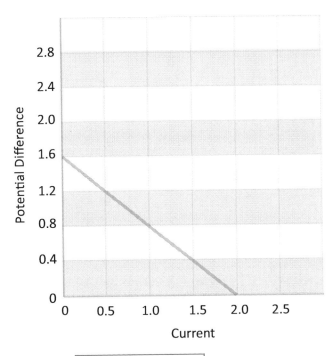

Answer [   ]

Question 8

The use of an earth-fault loop test is to make sure that...

A – Enough current is passable to open the protective device.

B – No charge can pass through.

C – The voltage through the circuit remains low.

D – The earth wire is connected safely and correctly.

Answer [   ]

Question 9

Below is a graph illustrating the terminal potential difference of the current of a battery. Use the graph to work out what the short circuit current would be.

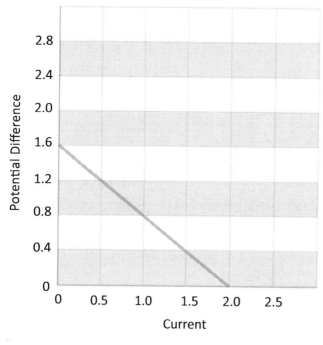

Answer [   ]

Question 10

A battery is measured to have the electromotive force of 8.4V, and the internal resistance of 1.2Ω. The battery is connected in a circuit to a resistor, which has the current flowing through it of 0.3A. Work out the lost volts of the battery.

A – 2.52V.

B – 1.5V.

C – 0.36V.

D – 9.6V.

Answer [   ]

Question 11

Ryan sketches a circuit. Within his electrical circuit, he places three resistors in series of one another. The only other component of the circuit is the battery which is 14 volts. Using Ryan's sketch below, work out the total current of the electrical circuit. Rounded to two decimal places.

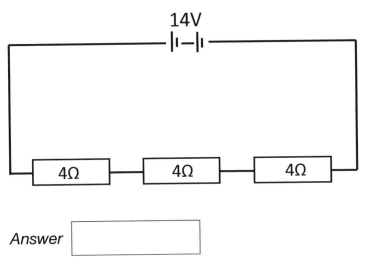

Answer

Question 12

Using Ryan's sketch in Question 11 above, work out the voltage drop across the middle resistor in the series.

A – 4.68Ω.

B – 0.12Ω.

C – 6.48V.

D – 4.68V.

Answer

Question 13

In your own words, explain the difference between direct and indirect contact in relation to electric shocks.

Question 14

A battery has an electromotive force of 3.50V. It is calculated to have the internal resistance of 0.48Ω. What is the potential difference expected if the circuit was an open circuit?

A – 0.48V.

B – 3.98V.

C – 3.50V.

D – 1.68V.

Answer

Question 15

If the current is interrupted in an inductive circuit, which of the following statements best explains why this could cause an issue?

A – Increased current.

B – Fluctuate the potential difference causing the e.m.f. to reduce.

C – Reduces electromotive force resulting in arching in the circuit.

D – Increased voltage.

Answer

Question 16

The main component in analogue electronics is the _ _ _ _ _ _ _ .

A – Fuse.

B – Transformer.

C – Op-amp.

D – Thermistor.

Answer

Question 17

An amplifier has an output of 3.45V. If the gain is 480, calculate the input. Rounded to two decimal places.

A – 0.179 mV.

B – 7.19 mV.

C – 9.17 mV.

D – 9 mV.

Answer

Question 18

The circuit drawn below illustrates the warning lamp being turned on and off, depending on the temperature. Label the arrows with the correct name of the electrical symbol.

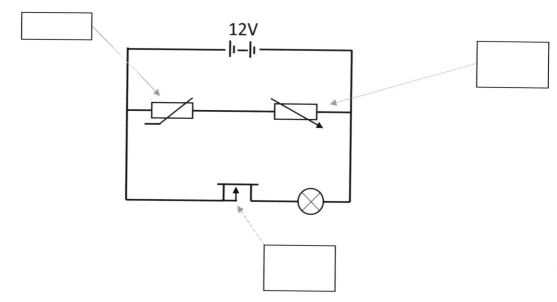

Question 19

As the temperature increases within the circuit, the resistance of the thermistor decreases. What will happen to the voltage across the thermistor if the temperature continues to increase?

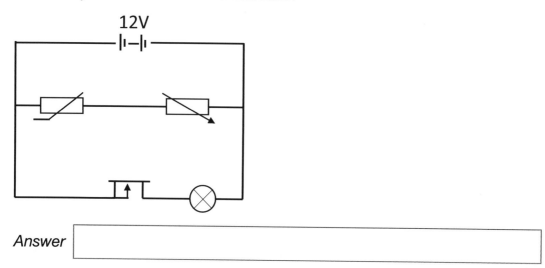

Answer

Question 20

Using the table below the circuit, which of the answers (A, B, C or D) shows the combination of conductors and/or insulators that would need to be placed in the gaps in order for the light to illuminate?

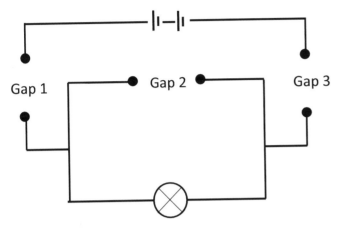

	Gap 1	Gap 2	Gap 3
A	Insulator	Conductor	Insulator
B	Conductor	Insulator	Conductor
C	Conductor	Conductor	Insulator
D	Insulator	Conductor	Conductor

Answer

Question 21

Elliott is a technician for a college. He is often building and sketching circuits and demonstrating electrical elements through theory and practice. Elliott has built a circuit consisting of a motor and a resistor.

What is the combined resistance of the resistor and the motor in Elliott's circuit? Rounded to two decimal places.

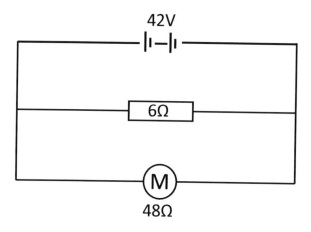

42V

6Ω

M

48Ω

A – 6.22Ω.

B – 5.33Ω.

C – 7.33Ω.

D – 9.26Ω.

Answer

Question 22

Michelle draws two circuits. Both of the circuits contains exactly the same components. The only difference between the circuits is that one is drawn in series (Circuit 1), and the other is drawn in parallel (Circuit 2).

Explain, using the box provided, how the change into a series circuit will affect the speed of the motor compared to the speed in Circuit 2.

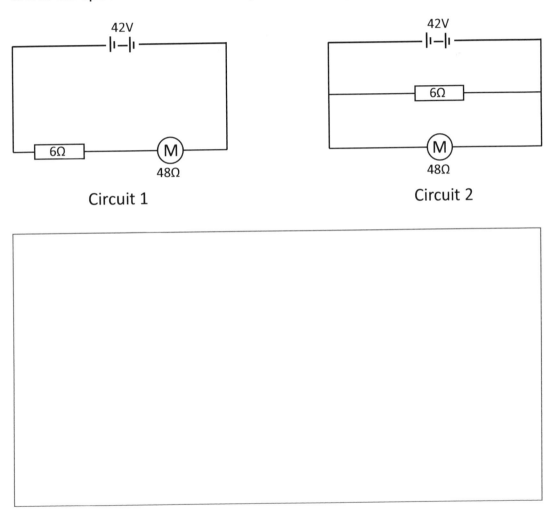

Circuit 1

Circuit 2

Question 23

A battery is measured to have the electromotive force of 9V, and the internal resistance of 3.2Ω. The battery is connected in a circuit to a resistor, which has the current of 0.6A flowing through it. Work out what are the lost volts of the battery.

Answer

Question 24

What are the minimum and maximum acceptable values if a resistor has the resistance of 23 kΩ and can tolerate ±15%?

Minimum value =

Maximum value =

Question 25

Calculate the total resistance of three parallel-connected resistors of 9Ω, 36Ω and 4Ω. Use the box below to show your workings out. Answer should be written to two decimal places.

ANSWERS TO ADVANCED – TEST SECTION 2

Q1. 270Ω

EXPLANATION = in order to work out the resistance, you should use the following equation:

R1 ÷ R2 = R3 ÷ R4

Step 1 = R1 and R2 = 180 ÷ 400 = 0.45. So, R3 ÷ R4 needs to be equivalent to 0.45.

Step 2 = R3 = (180 × 600) ÷ 400 = 270.

Step 3 = you can double check to make sure that you have the correct answer by doing the following:

180 ÷ 400 = 0.45.

270 ÷ 600 = 0.45.

Q2. D = 21 μF

EXPLANATION = in order to work out the effective capacitance, add up both capacitors' value:

8 + 13 = 21 μF.

Q3. A = the ammeter reading will increase; the voltmeter reading will decrease

EXPLANATION = if the resistance is decreased, this will make the current in the circuit increase. This is because there will be less resistance to restrict the flow. If the current gets bigger, the ammeter reading will increase. When more current flows through a circuit, the lost currents from the resistance increases. The force of the battery remains the same and so the potential difference decreases, and therefore the reading on the voltmeter will have decreased.

Q4. Your answer should read on the lines of the following:

Although both drills will ultimately complete the job, power is the rate which can be measured to determine how quickly work can be done, or even the use of energy that is required. That said, the hand drill will not only take longer because of the more work and force that needs to be applied, but it will also take longer to complete the same job. Whereas, an electric drill will complete the job more quickly simply because it has greater power.

Q5. C = 10Ω

EXPLANATION = in order to work out the value of R1, you should use the following method:

Step 1 = R1 ÷ R2 = R3 ÷ R4.

Step 2 = R1 ÷ 40 = 20 ÷ 80 = 0.25.

Step 3 = So, we need to find the value of R1 that once divided by 40, would give you 0.25.

Step 4 = 20 × 40 ÷ 80 = 10.

Step 5 = to make sure that you have the correct answer, you can double check that the value you have gives you 0.25. So, 10 ÷ 40 = 0.25. Therefore, 10 would be the correct answer.

Q6. D = internal resistance

EXPLANATION = the lost volts from the potential difference when the toy is turned off to the potential difference when the toy is turned on, is due to internal resistance. When current starts to flow through a circuit, there are lost volts across the internal resistance. This internal resistance was already in the circuit, i.e. all materials must have some resistance.

Q7. 0.8Ω

EXPLANATION = in order to work out the internal resistance from the graph illustrated, you need to divide the potential difference by the current.

So, 1.6 ÷ 2.0 = 0.8Ω.

Q8. A = enough current is passable to open the protective device

EXPLANATION = an earth-fault loop test is used to determine the current so that it is able to flow if an earth fault arises, which allows for the protective device to be opened.

Q9. 2.0A

EXPLANATION = in order to work out the short circuit current, this would be equal to the x axis. The current of the battery is 2.0, and so the short circuit current would also be 2.0A.

Q10. C = 0.36V

EXPLANATION = in order to work out the number of lost volts, you should use the following method:

Step 1 = lost volts = $0.3 \times 1.2 = 0.36V$.

Q11. 1.17A

EXPLANATION = in order to work out the total current in a series circuit, you should use the following method:

Total current = Volts ÷ Resistance = $4 + 4 + 4 = 12$.

So, $14V \div 12 = 1.166...$ To two decimal places = 1.17.

Q12. D = 4.68V

EXPLANATION = in order to work out the voltage drop, you should use the following equation:

Voltage drop = total current × resistance of the middle resistor in series (4Ω). So, $1.17 \times 4 = 4.68V$.

Please note, that although the digits in answer A are correct, it has the incorrect electrical symbol. The symbol will need to illustrate volts, not resistance.

Q13. The question asks you to explain the difference, so your answer should read something like this:

In terms of electrical shocks, direct contact is when a person or object becomes involved with 'live' wiring. Direct contact involves a person touching part of the electrical terminal or line conductor, whilst it is in operation, and therefore will receive an electrical shock.

This is different to indirect contact, whereby you can still receive an electrical shock despite not touching the 'live' wiring. Indirect contact can be defined as when a person comes into contact with a conductive part of the electrical system that has been exposed. This is usually because of a fault in the electrical system. It is not usually live, but becomes so when a fault or error occurs.

Q14. C = 3.50V

EXPLANATION = the potential difference in an open circuit is equivalent to the electromotive force of the battery. Therefore, the potential difference within this circuit would be 3.50V.

Q15. C = reduces electromotive force resulting in arching in the circuit.

EXPLANATION = if the current is interrupted in an inductive circuit, an issue may arise because it will reduce the electromotive force resulting in arching in the circuit.

Q16. C = op-amp

EXPLANATION = the main component of analogue electronics is an op-amp. Analogue electronics uses signals which are constantly changing to determine the physical quality of something, i.e. to measure the loudness of a sound. This is measured using an operational amplifier (op-amp).

Q17. B = 7.19 mV

EXPLANATION = in order to work out the input, you should use the following method:

Output ÷ gain = 3.45 ÷ 480 = 0.0071875.

0.0071875 × 1000 = 7.1875. To two decimal places = 7.19 mV.

Q18. The labels should look something like this:

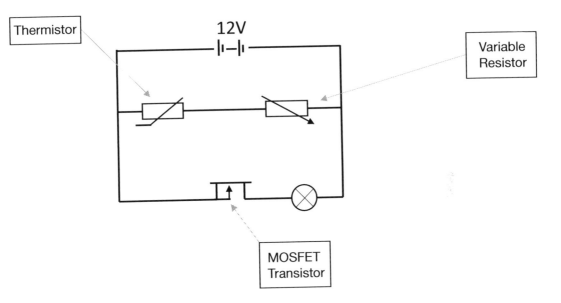

Thermistor

12V

Variable Resistor

MOSFET Transistor

Q19. The voltage will decrease

EXPLANATION = as the temperature increases, the resistance of the circuit will decrease and so the voltage will be decreased.

Q20. B = conductor, insulator, conductor

EXPLANATION = gaps 1 and 3 need to be conductors in order to allow the current to flow through to the other path of the circuit. Conductors allow for electrical currents to flow freely. Gap 2 would need to be an insulator because it completes the circuit, the current does not need to flow through.

Q21. B = 5.33Ω

EXPLANATION = in order to work out the total resistance, you should use the following method:

$$\frac{1}{6} + \frac{1}{48} = \frac{8+1}{48} = \frac{9}{48}$$

So, 48 ÷ 9 = 5.333. To two decimal places = 5.33Ω.

Q22. Your answer should read something like this:

Within Circuit 1, the speed of the motor will be reduced. This is because in the series circuit, it will take longer to get through each element of the circuit. The combined resistance of the circuit is now higher, and therefore it reduces the flow of the current. Ultimately, the motor has less power in Circuit 1 compared to the power in Circuit 2.

Q23. 1.92V

EXPLANATION = in order to work out the number of lost volts, you should use the following method:

Step 1 = lost volts = 0.6 × 3.2 = 1.92V.

Q24. Minimum = 19.55 kΩ, Maximum = 26.45 kΩ

EXPLANATION = 15% of 23 kΩ, or 23,000Ω.

Step 1 = 23,000 ÷ 100 × 15 = 3,450.

Step 2 = Minimum = 23,000 − 3,450 = 19,550Ω, or 19.55 kΩ.

Step 3 = Maximum = 23,000 + 3,450 = 26,450 Ω or 26.45 kΩ.

Q25. 2.57Ω

EXPLANATION = in order to work out the total resistance, use the following equation:

$$\frac{1}{R} = \frac{1}{R1} + \frac{1}{R2} + \frac{1}{R3}$$

$$\frac{1}{9} + \frac{1}{36} + \frac{1}{4} = \frac{4+1+9}{36} = \frac{14}{36}$$

So, 36 ÷ 14 = 2.57Ω.

ADVANCED –
TEST
SECTION 3

Question 1

Work out the maximum permissible current in a 2 kΩ resistor, if it had the watt rating of 0.5. Show your workings out.

Question 2

In the symbol for a semiconductor, the arrows are pointing in the direction of which of the following?

A – The negative connection.

B – The positive connection.

C – Conventional current flow.

D – The connection to the supply.

Answer

Question 3

In a bipolar-junction transistor, what are the three components of the resistor called?

A – Emitter, base, collector.

B – Diode, collector, base.

C – Emitter, diode, collector.

D – Source, emitter, diode.

Answer

Question 4

Fill in the table below with the names of three different capacitors and their function.

Capacitor	Function

Question 5

Explain the term 'magnetic flux'.

Question 6

The electrical component zener diodes, is commonly used in...

A – Oscillator circuits.

B – Power supply circuits.

C – Current-limiting circuits.

D – Amplified circuits.

Answer

Question 7

In the following circuit, identify what the symbol is representing.

input

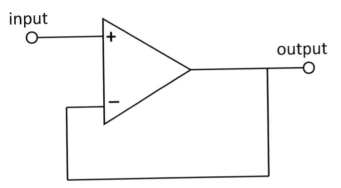

output

A – DC amplifiers.

B – Differential amplifier.

C – Voltage follower.

D – Current amplifier.

Answer

Question 8

The root mean square (RMS) value in an alternating current circuit is...

A – The peak value of a square-wave system.

B – Seldom used because it is difficult to calculate.

C – The effective value which is almost always given.

D – The square root of the average value.

Answer

Question 9

The effect which restricts the current flow in a conductor which is connected to an alternating voltage supply is called...

A – Induced electromotive force.

B – Inductive reactance.

C – Capacitance reactance.

D – Resistance.

Answer [   ]

Question 10

The formula for the power dissipated in the alternating current circuit which has a power factor of unity is...

A – $P = V^2R$.

B – $P = I^2R$.

C – $P = VIR$.

D – $P = R \div V^2$.

Answer [   ]

Question 11

Car batteries are often 12V, with six individual cells connected in series. What is the voltage of each cell in the car battery?

Answer

Question 12

Fossil fuels are a useful way to generate power. Which of the following is NOT needed in order to produce electrical power from a fossil fuel?

A – Heat.

B – Steam.

C – Dam.

D – Turbine.

Answer

Question 13

Lisa wants to listen to her portable FM radio. She realises that she needs batteries. The radio needs four AA batteries to power the radio. If an AA battery produces a potential difference of 1.5V, what is the total voltage of Lisa's FM radio?

A – 0.75V.

B – 1.5V.

C – 6.0V.

D – 3.0V.

Answer [   ]

Question 14

When a baby is born prematurely, they are usually placed in a heated incubator. The heating element in the incubator uses approximately 90 watts of power. It has a resistance of 1 kΩ. What is the voltage running through the heating element in the incubator?

A – 0.09 volts.

B – 300 volts.

C – 9 volts.

D – 0.3 volts.

Answer [   ]

Question 15

The Henry is a unit of measurement for which of the following?

A – Resistance.

B – Reactance.

C – Inductance.

D – Capacitance.

Answer

Question 16

A transformer has 30 turns on the primary and 330 on the secondary. If the input voltage is 400V, what is the output voltage going to be?

A – 36 volts.

B – 3600 volts.

C – 4400 volts.

D – 440 volts.

Answer

Question 17

Using the Wheatstone bridge circuit below, calculate the resistance of R3.

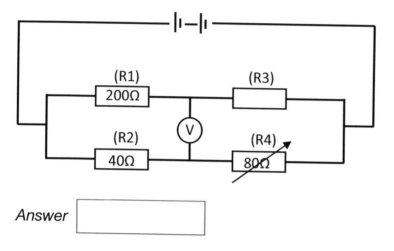

Answer

Question 18

The Wheatstone bridge circuit below is balanced, with R2 = 90Ω, R3 = 300Ω and R4 = 120Ω. What is the value or R1?

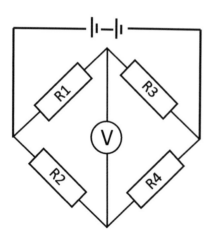

A	B	C	D
115Ω	50Ω	225Ω	90Ω

Question 19

After many years, people in the UK continue to leave their televisions on 'stand-by' mode when not in use. Explain why switching off televisions is better for the environment as opposed to leaving them on 'stand-by'.

Question 20

The lines of magnetic flux tend to be considered as having what direction?

A – Towards a south pole.

B – Towards a north pole.

C – South to north outside of a magnet.

D – North to south outside of a magnet.

Answer

Question 21

Which of the following circuits shows the correct connection for a voltmeter, a wattmeter and an ammeter?

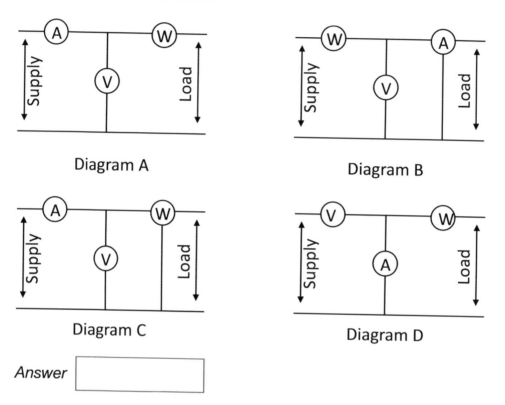

Diagram A   Diagram B

Diagram C   Diagram D

Answer

Question 22

The resistance of a conductor will be _____ when it is calculated by an alternating current supply as opposed to a direct current supply.

A – Lower.

B – Higher.

C – The same.

D – Fluctuating continuously.

Answer

Question 23

In electromagnets, the relationship between the electrical and magnetic waves will be...

A – Diagonal from one another.

B – In phase with one another.

C – Perpendicular with one another.

D – Unable to determine.

Answer

Question 24

A battery with an electromotive force of 7V produces a current of 3A around a circuit for 2 minutes. How much energy is provided in the circuit within this given time?

A	B	C	D
1850J	2000J	2520J	2150J

Question 25

A battery has an electromotive force of 6.25V. It is calculated to have the internal resistance of 0.64Ω. What is the potential difference expected if the circuit was an open circuit?

A – 0.64V.

B – 3.25V.

C – 4.5V.

D – 6.25V.

Answer

ANSWERS TO ADVANCED – TEST SECTION 3

Q1. 15.8 mA or 0.0158A

EXPLANATION = in order to work out the maximum permissible current, you should use the following method:

$$I = \sqrt{\frac{P}{R}} = \sqrt{\frac{0.5}{2000}} = 0.0158A.$$

$0.0158 \times 1000 = 15.8$ mA.

Q2. C = conventional current flow

EXPLANATION = in a semiconductor, the arrows are pointing in the direction of the conventional current flow of the circuit.

Q3. A = emitter, base, collector

EXPLANATION = in a bipolar-junction transistor, the three components of this electrical element are the emitter, the base and the collector.

Q4. Your answer should look something like this:

Capacitor	Function
Dielectric Capacitor	These types of capacitors function on the basis of continuous variations/fluctuations of capacitance. Usually required for tuning components such as transmitters, receivers and radios.
Film Capacitors	These capacitors consist of large groups of capacitors, each with a different dielectric element. They contain an insulating plastic film to carry electrodes.
Electrolytic Capacitors	These types of capacitors are usually used when a large capacitance value is needed. It uses a semi-liquid, like jelly or paste, to serve as another electrode.

Please note, that there are other capacitors that you could have used for your answer, and so if your answer is not included in the example answer above, you should check to see if it is correct via online research.

Q5. Your answer should read something like this:

Magnetic flux can be defined by the amount of magnetic field passing through a surface. It is the product of the magnetic field multiplied by the perpendicular surface area that it penetrates.

Q6. B = power supply circuits

EXPLANATION = zener diodes are used for specific reverse-breakdown voltage, which means that when the circuit is reverse-biased, the voltage through the diode remains the same.

Q7. C = voltage follower

EXPLANATION = a voltage follower is an operational amplifier which has the voltage gain of 1. The output voltage directly follows the input voltage, meaning that the output voltage will be the same as the input voltage. It provides no amplification to the voltage, hence the reason it is often referred to as a 'voltage follower'.

Q8. C = the effective value which is almost always given

EXPLANATION = the RMS value in an alternating current is the effective value which is almost always given.

Q9. B = inductive reactance

EXPLANATION = the effect which restricts the current flow in a conductor which is connected to alternating voltage supply is called inductive reactance.

Q10. B = P = I²R

EXPLANATION = you would need to use the following equation in order to work out the power dissipated in an alternating current which has a power factor of unity:

$P = I^2R$

Q11. 2V

EXPLANATION = if the car battery is made up of six individual cells in series, then each cell would be 2V. (2V × 6 cells = 12V.)

Q12. C = dam

EXPLANATION = a dam does not produce electrical power. They are used to produce power from water.

Q13.C = 6.0V

EXPLANATION = in order to work out the total voltage, you should use the following method:

1.5 + 1.5 + 1.5 + 1.5 = 6.0V. Voltages in series can be added to determine the total voltage.

Q14.B = 300 volts

EXPLANATION = in order to work out the voltage, you should use the following method:

$$\sqrt{P \times R} = \sqrt{\text{Power} \times \text{Resistance}} = \sqrt{90 \times 1000} = \sqrt{90{,}000} = 300 \text{ volts.}$$

Q15. C = inductance

EXPLANATION = the unit of Henry is used to measure inductance. For example, if current in a circuit changed its rate to 1 ampere per second, and the e.m.f. was measured as 1 volt, the inductance would be 1 henry.

Q16. C = 4400 volts

EXPLANATION = in order to work out the output voltage, you should use the following method:

330 ÷ 30 × 400 = 4400 volts.

Q17. R3 = 400Ω

EXPLANATION = in order to work out the resistance, you should use the following equation:

R1 ÷ R2 = R3 ÷ R4

Step 1 = R1 and R2 = 200 ÷ 40 = 5. So, R3 ÷ R4 needs to be equivalent to 5.

Step 2 = R3 = (200 × 80) ÷ 40 = 400.

Step 3 = you can double check to make sure that you have the correct answer by doing the following:

200 ÷ 40 = 5.

400 ÷ 80 = 5.

Q18. C = 225Ω

EXPLANATION = in order to work out the value of R1, you should use the following method:

Step 1 = R1 ÷ R2 = R3 ÷ R4.

Step 2 = R1 ÷ 90 = 300 ÷ 120 = 2.5.

Step 3 = So, we need to find the value of R1 that once divided by 90, would give you 2.5.

Step 4 = 300 × 90 ÷ 120 = 225.

Step 5 = to make sure that you have the correct answer, you can double check that the value you have gives you 2.5. So, 225 ÷ 90 = 2.5. Therefore, 225 would be the correct answer.

Q19. Your answer should read something like this:

If you leave a television on 'stand-by' mode, it continues to use electricity. This said, the television continues to generate electricity which ultimately produces carbon dioxide emissions. These carbon dioxide emissions contribute to global warming, and therefore impacts our environment.

Q20. D = north to south outside of a magnet

EXPLANATION = the lines of a magnetic flux are considered to have the direction of north to south outside of a magnet.

Q21. Diagram C

EXPLANATION = diagram C is the correct diagram that illustrates the correct connection of a voltmeter, a wattmeter and an ammeter.

Q22. B = higher

EXPLANATION = the resistance of a conductor will be higher when it is calculated by an alternating current supply as opposed to a direct current supply. This is because an alternating current has multiple paths to take, and therefore the resistance will be higher.

Q23. C = perpendicular with one another

EXPLANATION = in electromagnets, the relationship between the electrical and magnetic waves will be perpendicular with one another.

Q24. C = 2520J

EXPLANATION = in order to work out how much energy is transferred, you should use the following equation:

Total charge transferred/charge = current × time.

So, 3 × 2 × 60 = 360.

(volts × coulomb) = 7 × 360 = 2520J.

Q25. D = 6.25V

EXPLANATION = the potential difference in an open circuit is equivalent to the electromotive force of the battery. Therefore, the potential difference within this circuit would be 6.25V.

ADVANCED –
TEST
SECTION 4

Question 1

John is a physics student. At the moment, he is learning all about resistors. John is analysing one resistor which is labelled as being 10Ω ±10% with the power of 3 watts. John knows that this means the resistor could have the resistance anywhere between 9Ω and 11Ω.

Draw a circuit diagram which could illustrate how John could calculate the resistance. Within your diagram, you should include a 6V battery, a voltmeter and an ammeter.

Question 2

Using your circuit diagram in Question 1 above, if the reading for the voltage is 4.8V, and the current in the resistor is 0.8A, calculate the resistance.

A – 4Ω.

B – 3.84Ω.

C – 6Ω.

D – 5.6Ω.

Answer

Question 3

A microphone produces a signal of 36 mV. This is applied to an input of an amplifier. The output of the amplifier is 4V. What is the voltage gain of the amplifier? To the nearest whole number.

A – 111.

B – 120.

C – 112.

D – 110.

Answer [   ]

Question 4

What is the equivalent capacitance for $4\mu F$, $8\mu F$ and $16\mu F$ capacitors connected in a series? Rounded to two decimal places.

A – $2.28\mu F$.

B – $3.21\mu F$.

C – $1.29\mu F$.

D – $2.29\mu F$.

Answer [   ]

Question 5

One of the advantages of connecting in series is that each individual capacitor has potential difference _ _ _ _ _ _ the applied total voltage.

A – More than.

B – Less than.

C – The same as.

D – Cannot be determined.

Answer

Question 6

The capacitance of the following network circuit would be...

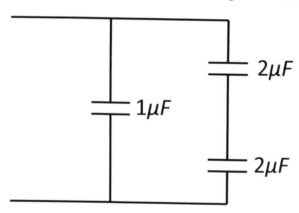

A – 4.1μF.

B – 5μF.

C – 2μF.

D – 1μF.

Answer

Question 7

Which of the following best describes the function of a transducer?

A – Decreases the voltage.

B – Increases the voltage.

C – A device that changes one form of energy into a different form of energy.

D – A device that is used to amplify small signals.

Answer

Question 8

What is the material called between the plates of a capacitor?

Answer

Question 9

A transformer has 70 turns on the primary and 240 on the secondary. If the input voltage is 300V, what is the output voltage going to be? Rounded to the nearest whole number.

A – 1029 volts.

B – 1028 volts.

C – 1030 volts.

D – 1000 volts.

Answer

Question 10

Peter draws a series circuit containing an inductor which has minor resistance. It is connected to a resistor of 14Ω, and connected to a 40V, 60Hz alternating current supply. If the current is 3A, work out the potential difference of the resistor.

A – 36 volts.

B – 14 volts.

C – 3 volts.

D – 42 volts.

Answer

Question 11

The total current flowing through the circuit below is...

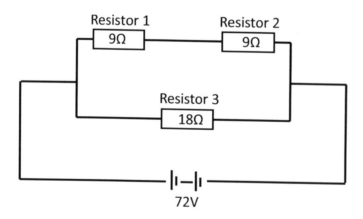

A – 4A.

B – 8A.

C – 16A.

D – 18A.

Answer

Question 12

Michael wants to connect an electrolytic capacitor in a circuit. An electrolytic capacitor is a type of capacitor that generates larger capacitance by using electrolytes. Michael is a professor in physics. He knows the important relationship of connecting an electrolytic capacitor in the correct polarity. Out of the following explanations, which best describes the probable result if an electrolytic capacitor is connected with the wrong polarity?

A – The capacitance will decrease.

B – The capacitor will burst.

C – The capacitance will increase.

D – There will no noticeable effect.

Answer

Question 13

Alice wants to know what the potential difference would be if 36J of energy is transferred when 6 electrical charges pass through. Show your workings out, and write your answer in the answer box provided.

Answer

Question 14

John uses a cell that has an electromotive force of 5V, with an internal resistance of 0.06Ω. This will be charged at 6A. Work out the terminal voltage that must be applied. Show your workings out.

Question 15

In the circuit below, you will see two sets of parallel resistors. The first set of resistors are 6Ω and 18Ω in parallel with one another. The second set of resistors consists of three resistors of 12Ω, 12Ω and 12Ω.

Work out the total resistance of the circuit, if the battery connected is powered by 18V.

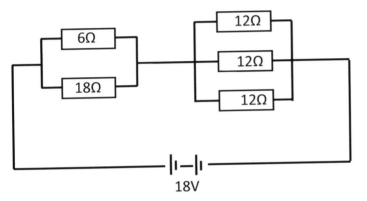

A	B	C	D
4.5Ω	6Ω	12.5Ω	8.5Ω

Answer

Question 16

What are the three colours for the cables in a three-phase system?

A – Red, blue and grey.

B – Black, red and grey.

C – Red, yellow and blue.

D – Black, brown and grey.

Answer

Question 17

A transformer has 25 turns on the primary and 550 on the secondary. If the input voltage is 300V, what is the output voltage going to be?

A – 3300 volts.

B – 6600 volts.

C – 6300 volts.

D – 9600 volts.

Answer

Question 18

What is the most usual conductor material used for cables?

A	B	C	D
Aluminium	Copper	Silver	Brass

Question 19

Fill in the table below with three types of materials used as insulators for cables and state an advantage.

Material	Function / Advantage

Question 20

Which of the following answers best describes the explanation below?

A device which is used for the purpose of producing signals.

A	B	C	D
Oscillator	Transformer	Polarity	Bipolar junction

Question 21

What are the minimum and maximum acceptable values if a resistor has the resistance of 28 kΩ and can tolerate ±30%?

Minimum value =

Maximum value =

Question 22

In which of the following circuits would the ammeter show the greatest current?

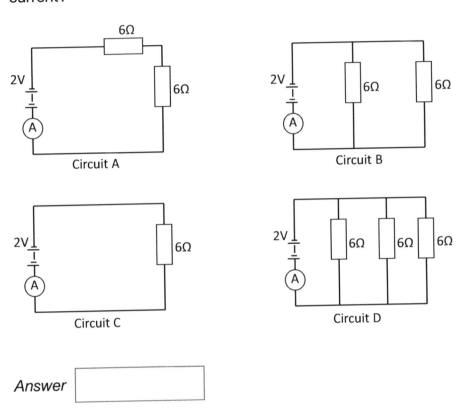

Question 23

The total resistance of multiple resistors which are connected in parallel is...

A – Bigger than the biggest resistance in the circuit.

B – Equal to the smallest resistance.

C – Equal to the largest resistance.

D – Smaller than the smallest resistance in the circuit.

Answer

Question 24

Three 30Ω resistors are connected in parallel. These resistors are connected across a 9 volt battery. What is the current?

A	B	C	D
0.3A	0.6A	0.9A	0.1A

Question 25

The diagram below shows three resistors R1, R2 and R3, connected to a 27V battery. What is the potential drop across R2, if voltmeter V1 reads 6A and V3 reads 3A?

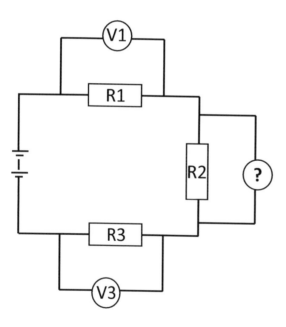

A – 6A.

B – 9A.

C – 18A.

D – 27A.

Answer

ANSWERS TO ADVANCED – TEST SECTION 4

Q1. Your diagram should look like the following:

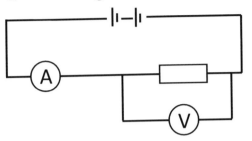

Q2. C = 6Ω

EXPLANATION = in order to work out the resistance, you would use the following equation:

$R = V \div I$

$R = 4.8 \div 0.8 = 6Ω$.

Q3. A = 111

EXPLANATION = in order to work out the voltage gain, you need to use the following method:

$4 \div 0.036 = 111.111$

To the nearest whole number = 111.

Q4. D = 2.29μF

EXPLANATION = in order to work out the equivalent capacitance, you should use the following method:

$$\frac{1}{Ct} = \frac{1}{C1} + \frac{1}{C2} + \frac{1}{C3}$$

$$\frac{1}{4} + \frac{1}{8} + \frac{1}{16} = \frac{4+2+1}{16} = \frac{7}{16}$$

So, $16 \div 7 = 2.2857$. To two decimal places = 2.29μF.

Q5. B = less than

EXPLANATION = One of the advantages of connecting in series is that each individual capacitor has the potential difference less than the applied total voltage. This means that capacitors with low voltage which are connected in series are able to form a higher voltage.

Q6. C = 2μF

EXPLANATION = the capacitance in the network circuit would be 2μF.

Q7. C = a device that changes one form of energy into a different form of energy

EXPLANATION = a transducer is an electrical device that changes one form of energy into a different form of energy.

Q8. Dielectric

EXPLANATION = the material between the plates of a conductor is called dielectric. A dielectric is an insulating material that can be divided by an electrical field.

Q9. A =1029 volts

EXPLANATION = in order to work out output voltage, you should use the following method:

$240 \div 70 \times 300 = 1028.57$

Rounded to the nearest whole number = 1029.

Q10. D = 42 volts

EXPLANATION = in order to work out the potential difference, you should use the following equation:

$V_R = I \times R = 14 \times 3 = 42$ volts.

Q11. B = 8A

EXPLANATION = in order to work out the total current, you should use the following equations:

$$\frac{1}{R} = \frac{1}{R1+2} + \frac{1}{R3} = \frac{1}{18} + \frac{1}{18} = \frac{2}{18}$$

So, $18 \div 2 = 9$.

$72V \div 9 = 8A$.

Q12. B = the capacitor will burst

EXPLANATION = if an electrolytic capacitor is connected with the incorrect polarity, it is likely that the capacitor will burst. A polarised element in a circuit needs to be connected correctly in order for the circuit to function. The component might have several pins which can only be connected to a circuit in one direction. If it is connected otherwise, this will likely cause the capacitor to smoke, swell or burst.

Q13. 6V

EXPLANATION = in order to work out the potential difference, you should use the following method:

$36 \div 6 = 6V$.

Q14. 5.36V

EXPLANATION = your workings out should look something like this:

Step 1 = $5 + (6 \times 0.06)$

Step 2 = $5 + (0.36)$

Step 3 = $5.36V$.

Q15. D = 8.5Ω

EXPLANATION = in order to work out the total resistance in the circuit, use the following method:

Step 1 = first you should work out the first set of resistors:

$$\frac{1}{6} + \frac{1}{18} = \frac{3+1}{18} = \frac{4}{18}$$

So, $18 \div 4 = 4.5$

Step 2 = now work out the second set of resistors:

$$\frac{1}{12} + \frac{1}{12} + \frac{1}{12} = \frac{3}{12}$$

So, $12 \div 3 = 4$.

Step 3 = to work out the total resistance, add both of these up = $4.5 + 4 = 8.5Ω$.

Q16. D = black, brown and grey

EXPLANATION = the three standard colours of a three-phase system are black, brown and grey.

Q17. B = 6600 volts

EXPLANATION = in order to work out the output voltage, you should use the following method:

$550 \div 25 \times 300 = 6600$ volts.

Q18. B = copper

EXPLANATION = the most usual conductor used for cables is copper.

Q19. Your table should look something like this:

Material	Function / Advantage
Polyvinyl chloride	A robust, plastic material that can be changed if temperature exceeds a certain level. It is resistant to weathering and sunlight.
Silicone rubber	Good weathering properties. It remains elasticated even over certain temperatures. Resists water and mineral oils.
Glass fibre	Glass fibre can be used to insulate cords which are often used for high temperature lighting appliances.

Please note! The above list is not exhaustive, and therefore further research may be required to check your answers.

Q20. A = oscillator

EXPLANATION = an oscillator is a device that is used to produce signals. This often includes computers, clocks, radios and watches. These have a periodic fluctuation between two things which are based on the changes in energy.

Q21. Minimum = 19.6 kΩ, Maximum = 36.4 kΩ

EXPLANATION = 30% of 28 kΩ, or 28,000Ω.

Step 1 = 28,000 ÷ 100 × 30 = 8,400.

Step 2 = Minimum = 28,000 – 8,400 = 19,600Ω, or 19.6 kΩ.

Step 3 = Maximum = 28,000 + 8,400 = 36,400Ω or 36.4 kΩ.

Q22. Circuit D

EXPLANATION = circuit D's ammeter would have the greatest current reading.

Q23. D = smaller than the smallest resistance in the circuit

EXPLANATION = the total resistance of multiple resistors which are connected in parallel is smaller than the smallest resistance in the circuit.

Q24. C = 0.9A

EXPLANATION = in order to work out the total current, use the following method:

Step 1 = each resistor is 30Ω.

Step 2 = resistor 1 = 9 ÷ 30 = 0.3. Resistor 2 = 9 ÷ 30 = 0.3. Resistor 3 = 9 ÷ 30 = 0.3.

Step 3 = 0.3 + 0.3 +0.3 = 0.9A.

Q25. C = 18A

EXPLANATION = to work out the potential drop across resistor 2, you should use the following method:

Step 1 = R1 + R3 = 6 + 3 = 9.

Step 2 = 27 – 9 = 18A.

A FEW
FINAL WORDS...

You have now reached the end of your Electrical Comprehension testing guide, and no doubt feel more competent regarding these types of testing questions. We hope you have found this guide to be an invaluable insight into the different types of electrical elements and components, and have bettered your overall understanding of electrical comprehension.

For any test, we believe that there are a few things to remember in order to help you perform at your best…

REMEMBER – THE THREE Ps!

1. **Preparation.** This may seem obvious, but you will be surprised at how many people fail psychometric testing because they lacked preparation and knowledge regarding their assessment. You want to do your utmost to ensure you have the best possible chance of succeeding. Be sure to do as much preparation as possible prior to your assessment to ensure you are fully aware and 100% prepared to complete the test successfully. Like anything, the more you practice, the more likely you are to succeed.

2. **Perseverance.** You are far more likely to succeed at something if you constantly set out to achieve it. Everybody encounters times whereby they are setback or find obstacles in the way of their goals. The important thing to remember when this happens, is to use those setbacks and obstacles as a way of progressing. It is what you do with your past experiences that helps to determine your success in the future. If you fail at something, consider *why* you have failed. This will allow you to improve and enhance your performance for next time.

3. **Performance.** Performance is a great word! Your performance will determine whether or not you are likely to succeed. Attributes that are often associated with performance are self-belief, motivation and commitment. Self-belief is an important concept for anything you do in life. It allows you to recognise your own abilities and skills and believe that you can do well. Believing that you can do well is half the battle! Being fully motivated and committed is often difficult for some people, but we can assure you that nothing is gained without hard work and determination. If you want to succeed, you will need to put in that extra time and hard work.

Work hard, stay focused, and be what you want!

Good luck with your Electrical Comprehension Tests. We would like to wish you the best of luck with all your future endeavours.

The how2become team

The How2become team

how2become

Get more books, manuals, online tests and training courses at:

www.how2become.com

Made in the USA
Middletown, DE
23 January 2020

83608401R00106